Everyday Mathematics®

Journal 2

**The University of Chicago
School Mathematics Project**

EVERYDAY LEARNING™

Chicago, Illinois

Authors
Max Bell
Robert Balfanz
William Carroll
Robert Hartfield
James McBride
Peter Saecker

Teachers in Residence
Amy Dillard
Kathleen Pitvorec
Denise Porter
John Wilson

Everyday Learning Development Staff
Editorial: John Bretzlauf, Patrick Carroll,
   Rosi Marshall, Steve Mico, Michael Murphy,
   Adam W. Sugerman
Production/Design: Jess Schaal, Norma Underwood
Revision Content Reviewer: Fred Bartling

Additional Credits
Curtis Design
Chris Sheban (*cover*)

Contributors
Diane Barrie (*selected art*)
James Flanders
Sharon McHugh
William Pattison
Shelia Sconiers
Laura Sunseri
Mary Wilson
Carl Zmola
Theresa Zmola (*original design*)

Field-Test Teachers
Tammy Belgrade
Ann Hemwall
Lee Kornhauser
Judy Korshak-Samuels
Joseph C. Liptak
Janet M. Meyers
Susan Mieli
Donna Nowatzki
Mary O'Boyle
Juile Olson
Loretta Rice
Michelle Schiminsky
Kevin J. Smith
Theresa Sparlin
Kim Van Haitsma

Acknowledgments

Page 300 Map from *Beginnings of the American Rectangular Land Survey, 1784–1800* by William D. Pattison. Reprinted by permission of the author. Page 360 Photo: Old Faithful, Yellowstone National Park, Wyoming. V. Lefteroff/FPG International.

This material is based upon work supported by the National Science Foundation under Grant No. ESI-9252984. Any opinions, findings, and conclusions or recommendations expressed in this material are those of the authors and do not necessarily reflect the views of the National Science Foundation.

Contents

Unit 8: Algebra Concepts and Skills

Unit 9: Fractions and Ratios

Unit 10: Volume

Unit 11: Fraction Multiplication, Percents, and Rates

Activity Sheets

Math Message: Earth's Surface Covered by Water

Percent of Earth's surface that is covered by water:

My estimate: _____

A Sampling Experiment

My location is at latitude _____ longitude _____

My location is on   land   water.   (Circle one.)

What fraction of the class has a water location? _____

Percent of Earth's surface that is covered by water:

My class's estimate: _____

Follow-up

Your teacher can tell you the actual percent of Earth's surface that is covered by water, or you can look it up in a reference book.

Percent of Earth's surface that is covered by water:

Actual figure: _____

How does your class's estimate compare to the actual figure?

_____

_____

Note: This method of sampling usually gives results that are close to the actual value. However, it sometimes gives results that are very different.

Plotting a Turtle

Points on a coordinate grid are named by ordered
number pairs. The first number in an ordered number
pair locates the point along the horizontal axis.
The second number locates the point along the
vertical axis. To mark a point on a coordinate grid,
first go right (or left) on the
horizontal axis. Then go up
(or down) from there.

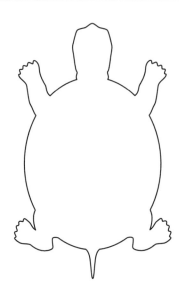

Plot an outline of the turtle
on the graph below. Start
with the nose, at point (8,12).

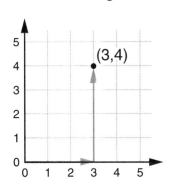

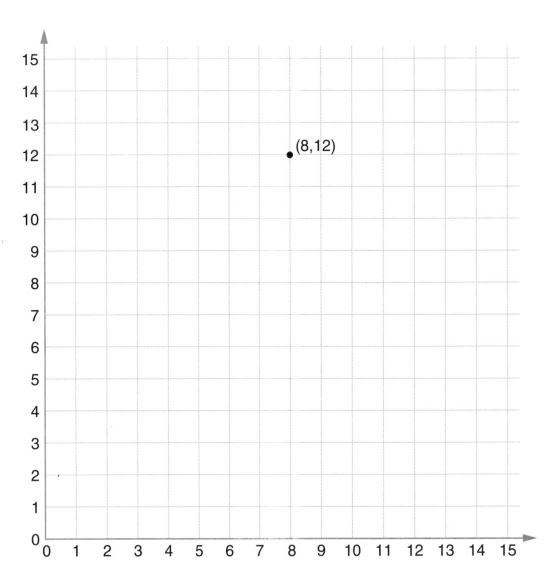

Use with Lesson 64.

Hidden Treasure

Materials ❑ *Hidden Treasure* game board for each player
(a gameboard has 2 grids); pencil; red pen or crayon

Number of players 2

Object Each player "hides" a grid point. Each player tries to "find" the other player's hidden point.

Directions

1. Players A and B each write on their own copy of a *Hidden Treasure* game board. They sit so that neither player can see what the other is writing.

2. Using a red pen or crayon, each player secretly marks a point on Grid 1. These are the "hidden" points.

3. Player A tries to guess the location of Player B's hidden point by naming an ordered number pair. For example, to name (2,5), Player A might say, "2 comma 5."

4. If Player B's hidden point is at that location, Player A wins the game.

5. If the hidden point is not at that location, Player B marks the guess in pencil on Grid 1. Then Player B counts the fewest number of "square sides" needed to travel from the hidden point to the guessed point. Player B tells this number to Player A.

6. Player A records this number at the guessed location on Grid 2. Player A can use this information to improve the next guess.

7. Player B names an ordered number pair for the location of Player A's hidden point and proceeds as above.

8. Play continues until a player guesses the location of a hidden point.

Example:

Player B's hidden point is (3,7). Player A guesses the point (1,2). Player B marks this point on Grid 1. Player B tells Player A that the guess is 7 "square sides" away. Player A writes 7 at the point (1,2) on Grid 2. It is now Player B's turn to guess the point that Player A has hidden.

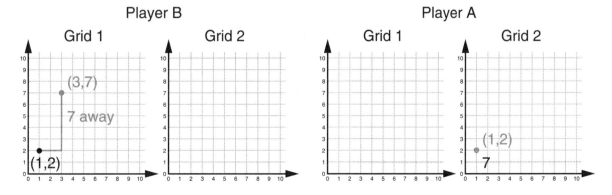

Hidden Treasure Gameboards

Use Grids 1 and 2 to play a game.

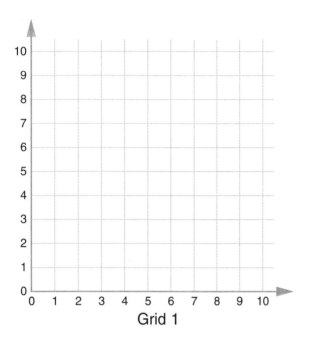

Grid 1

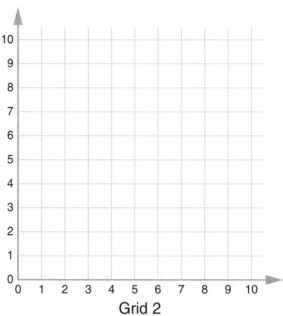

Grid 2

Use Grids 1 and 2 to play another game.

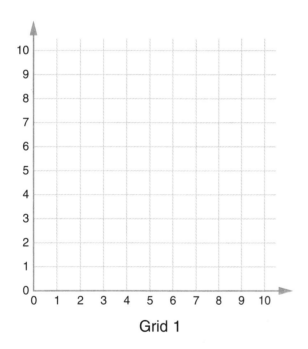

Grid 1

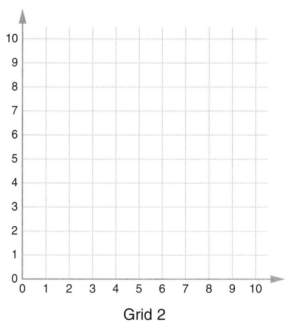

Grid 2

Math Boxes 64

1. Solve.

   a.   429
      + 813

   b.   729
      + 502

   c.   914
      + 986

   d.   235
      − 189

   e.   473
      − 306

   f.   605
      − 493

2. Complete the table.

Fraction	Decimal	Percent
$\frac{2}{3}$		
	0.95	
		43%
$\frac{3}{5}$		
	0.8	

3. Draw and label angle *TIN*. The measure of ∠*TIN* is 84°.

4. Find the whole set.

   a. 4 is $\frac{1}{8}$ of the set. _____

   b. 4 is $\frac{2}{5}$ of the set. _____

   c. 9 is $\frac{3}{7}$ of the set. _____

   d. 5 is $\frac{1}{3}$ of the set. _____

   e. 12 is $\frac{3}{8}$ of the set. _____

5. Measure line segment *IT* to the nearest tenth of a centimeter.

I •———————————————————• T

$\overline{IT}$ is about _____ cm.

Math Message: Plotting a Map

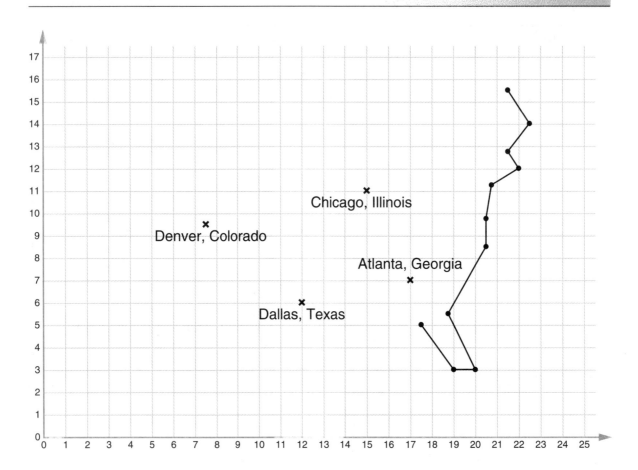

1. Plot the following ordered number pairs on the grid:

   (21,14) (17,11) (17,13) (15,14) (2,16) (1,11) (2,8) (3,6) (7.5,5.5) (11,2.5) (12.5,4)

   Connect all the points in the same order they were plotted. Also connect
   (12.5,4) to (17.5,5) and (21.5,15.5) to (21,14). When you have finished, you
   should see an outline map of the continental United States.

2. Write an ordered number pair to locate each city.

   Chicago, Illinois (_____,_____)   Atlanta, Georgia (_____,_____)

   Dallas, Texas (_____,_____)   Denver, Colorado (_____,_____)

3. Plot each city on the grid and write in the city name.

   Billings, Montana (7.5,13)   Salt Lake City, Utah (5.5,10.5)

4. The U.S.-Mexican border is shown by line segments from (3,6) to (7.5,5.5) and
   from (7.5,5.5) to (11,2.5). Write the border name on the grid.

Math Boxes 65

1. Complete the "What's My Rule?" table and state the rule.

	in	out
Rule	3	
	8	40
	$\frac{1}{2}$	
		50
	4	

2. Tell the value of the following digits in 6,034,291.

a. 9 _____

b. 4 _____

c. 6 _____

d. 2 _____

e. 3 _____

3. Raphael bought 14 pounds of meat to make hamburgers at the Fourth of July barbecue. He made 5 hamburgers from each pound. Buns come in packages of 8. How many packages of buns did Raphael need? _____

Explain your answer. _____

4. Tell whether each number is prime or composite.

a. Number of hours in $\frac{1}{3}$ of a day. _____

b. Number of minutes in $\frac{1}{12}$ of an hour. _____

c. Number of weeks in $\frac{1}{4}$ of a year. _____

d. Number of months in $\frac{2}{3}$ of a year. _____

e. Number of days in $\frac{3}{7}$ of a week. _____

5. Fill in the missing values on each number line.

a.

b.

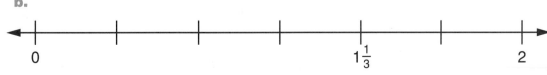

Sailboat Graphs

1. Using the ordered number pairs listed in the column titled "Original Sailboat" in the table below, plot the ordered number pairs on the grid titled "Original Sailboat" on the next page.

   Connect the points in the same order that you plot them. You should see the outline of a sailboat.

2. Fill in the missing ordered number pairs in the last three columns of the table. Use the rule given in each column to calculate the ordered number pairs.

Original Sailboat	New Sailboat 1 Rule: Double each number of the original pair.	New Sailboat 2 Rule: Double the first number of the original pair.	New Sailboat 3 Rule: Double the second number of the original pair.
(8,1)	(16,2)	(16,1)	(8,2)
(5,1)	(10,2)	(10,1)	(5,2)
(5,7)	(10,14)	(10,7)	(5,14)
(1,2)	(__,__)	(__,__)	(__,__)
(5,1)	(__,__)	(__,__)	(__,__)
(0,1)	(__,__)	(__,__)	(__,__)
(2,0)	(__,__)	(__,__)	(__,__)
(7,0)	(__,__)	(__,__)	(__,__)
(8,1)	(__,__)	(__,__)	(__,__)

3. Plot the ordered number pairs for New Sailboat 1 on the next page. Connect the points in the same order that you plot them.

   Then plot the ordered number pairs for New Sailboat 2 and connect the points.

   Finally, plot the ordered number pairs for New Sailboat 3 and connect the points.

Sailboat Graphs (continued)

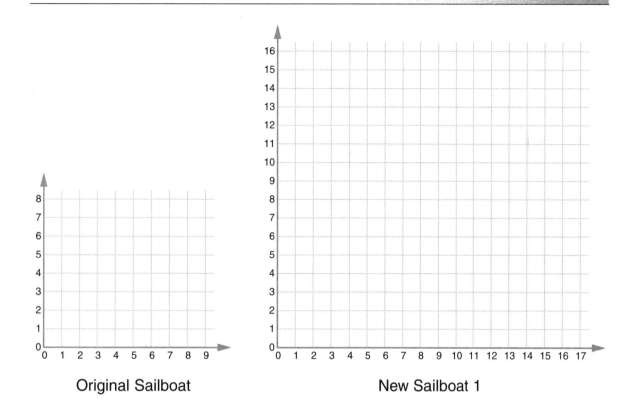

Original Sailboat   New Sailboat 1

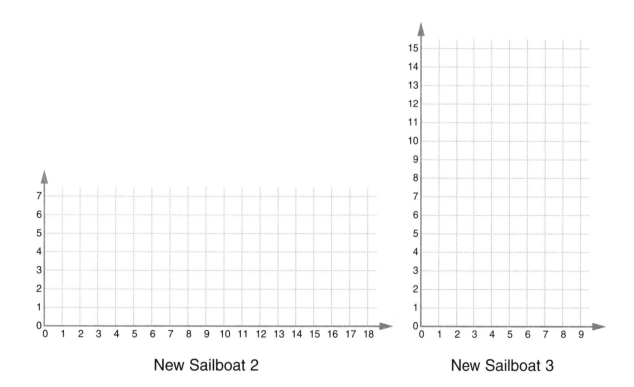

New Sailboat 2   New Sailboat 3

Use with Lesson 65.

More Sailboat Graphs

1. Using the ordered number pairs listed in the column titled "Original Sailboat" in the table below, plot the ordered number pairs on the grid on the next page.

   Connect the points in the same order they were plotted. You should see the outline of a sailboat. Write "original" in the sail.

2. Fill in the missing ordered number pairs in the last three columns of the table. Use the rule given in each column to calculate the ordered number pairs.

Original Sailboat	New Sailboat 1 Rule: Add 10 to the first number of the original number pair.	New Sailboat 2 Rule: Change the first number of the original pair to the opposite number.	New Sailboat 3 Rule: Change the second number of the original pair to the opposite number.
(9,3)	(19,3)	(−9,3)	(9,−3)
(6,3)	(16,3)	(−6,3)	(6,−3)
(6,9)	(16,9)	(−6,9)	(6,−9)
(2,4)	(___,___)	(___,___)	(___,___)
(6,3)	(___,___)	(___,___)	(___,___)
(1,3)	(___,___)	(___,___)	(___,___)
(3,2)	(___,___)	(___,___)	(___,___)
(8,2)	(___,___)	(___,___)	(___,___)
(9,3)	(___,___)	(___,___)	(___,___)

3. Plot the ordered number pairs for New Sailboat 1 on the next page. Connect the points in the same order that you plot them. Write "1" in the sail. Then plot the ordered number pairs for New Sailboat 2 and connect the points. Write "2" in the sail. Finally, plot the ordered number pairs for New Sailboat 3 and connect the points. Write "3" in the sail.

More Sailboat Graphs (continued)

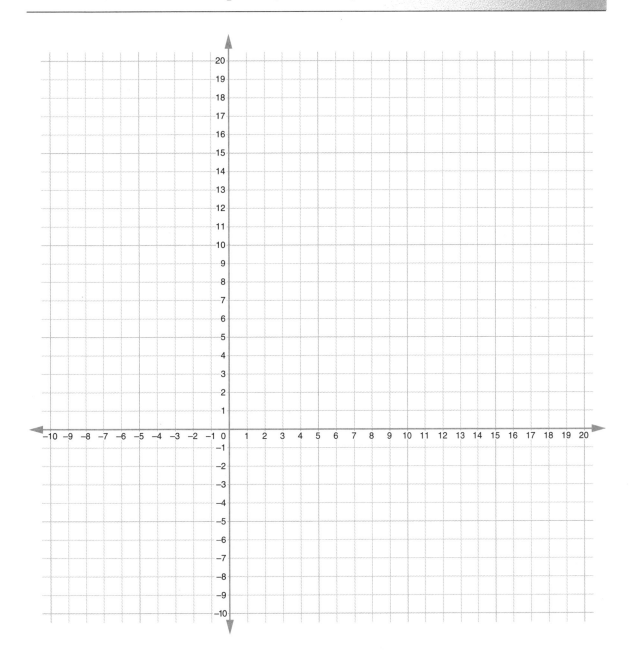

4. Use the following rule to create a new sailboat figure on the grid above. Label it "4."

   Rule: Add 10 to the second number of the original pair. Leave the first number unchanged.

   Try to plot the new coordinates without listing them.

Advanced Hidden Treasure **Gameboards**

Use Grids 1 and 2 below to play a game.

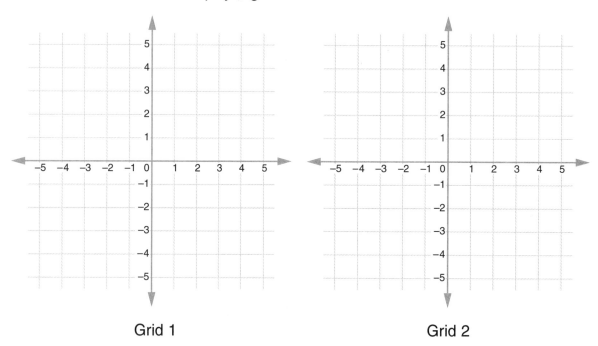

Grid 1   Grid 2

Use Grids 1 and 2 below to play another game.

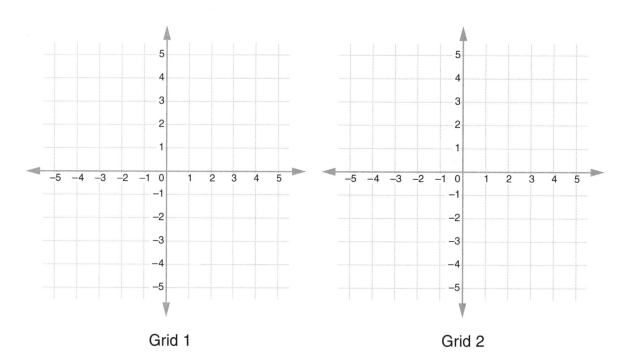

Grid 1   Grid 2

Math Boxes 66

1. Find the difference between the highest and lowest temperatures recorded in each state.

	Lowest	Highest	Difference
a. Alaska	−80°F	100°F	_____
b. Arizona	−40°F	127°F	_____
c. Nebraska	−47°F	118°F	_____
d. South Dakota	−58°F	120°F	_____

Source: *World Almanac.*

2. Find the radius of the circle.

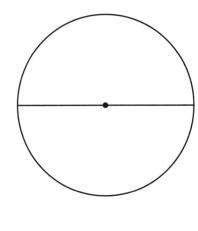

_____

3. What is the perimeter of the rectangle?

12 units

8 units

_____

4. Divide.

a. 843 ÷ 28 → _____

b. 279 ÷ 17 → _____

c. 396 ÷ 43 → _____

d. 504 ÷ 24 = _____

e. 755 ÷ 31 → _____

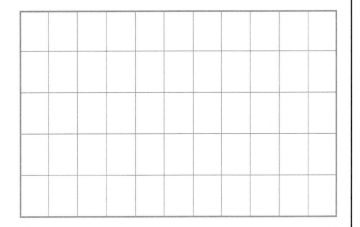

Math Message: A Mental Calculation Strategy

When you are multiplying mentally, it is sometimes helpful to double one factor and halve the other factor.

Example 1: 45 * 12 = ?

1. Double 45 and halve 12:
   45 * 12 = 90 * 6.

2. Multiply 90 and 6:
   90 * 6 = 540.

Example 3: 75 * 28 = ?

1. Double 75 to get 150 and halve 28 to get 14.

2. Double again to get 300 and halve again to get 7.

3. 75 * 28 = 300 * 7 = 2100.

Example 2: 18 * 15 = ?

1. Halve 18 and double 15:
   18 * 15 = 9 * 30.

2. Multiply 9 and 30:
   9 * 30 = 270.

Example 4: 35 * 14 = ?

Your turn. Use the doubling and halving strategy to calculate mentally.

Units of Area

Imagine the following situations:

- You ask your teacher how long it takes her to get to school in the morning. She replies, "About 1800 seconds."

- You look in an encyclopedia to find the weight of a tiger. The encyclopedia states, "A typical tiger weighs about 8000 ounces."

- Your physical education teacher would like to know your height. You answer, "I am 0.0015 kilometers tall."

Do these measurements seem strange to you? Why?

_____

_____

_____

_____

Units of Area (continued)

We use **units,** such as seconds, ounces, and kilometers, to report measurements of time, weight, and distance. In any situation, we have a choice of which units to use. Some choices make more sense than others. In the examples, it is correct to say 1800 seconds, 8000 ounces, and 0.0015 kilometers, but better answers would be 30 minutes, 500 pounds, and 150 centimeters (or 1.5 meters).

Area is the measure of a region inside a closed boundary. The area of a region is the number of unit squares and fractions of unit squares needed to cover the region without overlaps and without gaps between the unit squares, the fractions of unit squares, and the boundary.

Area is generally reported in **square units.** The most frequently used units of area for small regions are square inches, square feet, square yards, square centimeters, and square meters. For large land areas, acres or square miles are used in the United States; hectares or square kilometers are used in most other countries.

The area of a field-hockey field is reported in three different ways below.

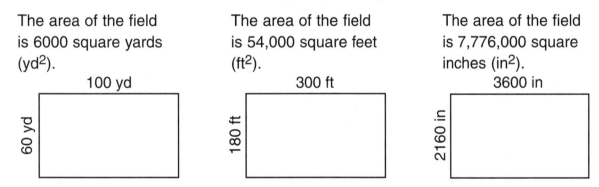

The area of the field is 6000 square yards (yd^2).

The area of the field is 54,000 square feet (ft^2).

The area of the field is 7,776,000 square inches (in^2).

Each of the measurements above is correct. However, you will probably agree that giving the area in square inches really doesn't give us a good idea about the size of the field. It is hard to imagine 7,776,000 of anything!

For the remainder of this unit, you will use a variety of strategies and formulas to find the areas of rectangles, triangles, parallelograms, and circles, as well as the areas of some oddly-shaped polygons. To name the areas in an understandable way, you will use a variety of units.

Area of Rectangles

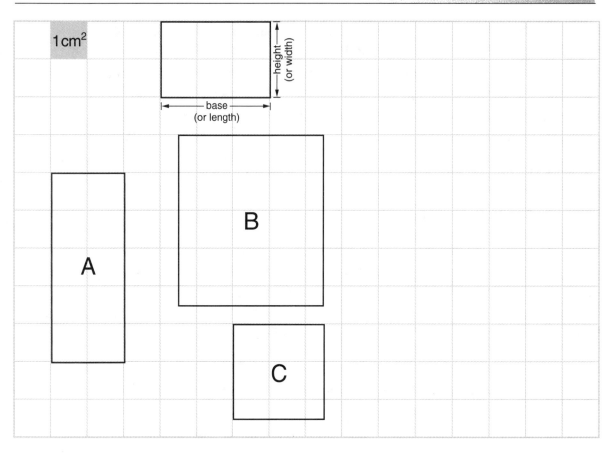

1. Fill in the table. Draw rectangles D, E, and F on the grid.

Rectangle	Base (length)	Height (width)	Area
A	_____ cm	_____ cm	_____ cm^2
B	_____ cm	_____ cm	_____ cm^2
C	_____ cm	_____ cm	_____ cm^2
D	6 cm	_____ cm	12 cm^2
E	3.5 cm	_____ cm	14 cm^2
F	3 cm	_____ cm	10.5 cm^2

2. Write a formula for finding the area of a rectangle.

Area = _____

Use with Lesson 67.

Area Problems

1. A bedroom floor is 12 feet by 15 feet (4 yards by 5 yards).

   Floor area = _____ square feet.

   Floor area = _____ square yards.

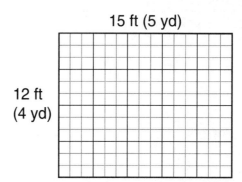

15 ft (5 yd)

12 ft (4 yd)

2. Imagine that you want to buy carpet for the bedroom in Problem 1. The carpet comes on a roll that is 6 feet (2 yards) wide. The carpet salesperson unrolls the carpet to the length you want and cuts off your piece. How long a piece will you need to cover the bedroom floor? _____

6 ft (2 yd)

3. Calculate the areas for the figures below.

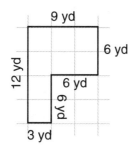

9 yd

12 yd

6 yd

6 yd

6 yd

3 yd

Area = _____ yd²

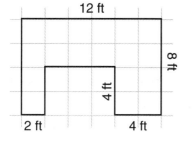

12 ft

8 ft

4 ft

2 ft   4 ft

Area = _____ ft²

4. Fill in the missing lengths for the figures below.

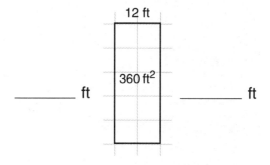

12 ft

360 ft²

_____ ft   _____ ft

_____ ft

_____ yd

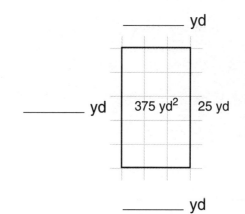

_____ yd   375 yd²   25 yd

_____ yd

Math Boxes 67

1. Add or subtract.

    a. 1427 − 1039 = _____

    b. 2570 − 671 = _____

    c. 382 − 108 = _____

    d. 479 + 634 = _____

    e. 458 + 759 = _____

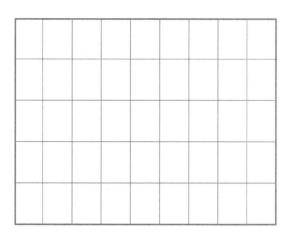

2. Complete the table.

Fraction	Decimal	Percent
$\frac{7}{10}$	0.7	
$\frac{3}{8}$		
		100%
	0.625	
		$33\frac{1}{3}\%$

3. Measure each angle.

    a. ∠*LID* measures about

    _____°.

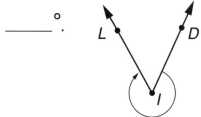

    b. ∠*FUN* measures about

    _____°.

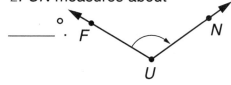

4. There are 36 stamps in each package. How many stamps are there in

    a. $\frac{3}{4}$ of the package? _____

    b. $\frac{5}{6}$ of the package? _____

    c. $\frac{2}{9}$ of the package? _____

    d. $\frac{7}{12}$ of the package? _____

    e. $\frac{2}{3}$ of the package? _____

5. Draw a line segment that is about 24 millimeters long.

About how many inches long is the line segment?

_____

Math Message: Personal References

In *Fourth Grade Everyday Mathematics*, you found **personal references** for metric and U.S. customary units of length, weight, and capacity. These references are familiar objects whose sizes approximate standard measures. For example, for many people the distance across the tip of their smallest finger is about 1 centimeter.

Now you are working with **area,** so try to find personal references for area units.

Spend some time searching through your workspace or classroom to find common objects that have areas of 1 square inch, 1 square foot, 1 square yard, 1 square centimeter, and 1 square meter. The areas do not have to be exact, but they should be reasonable estimates. Ask a friend to look for references with you. Try to find more than one reference for each measure.

Personal References for Common Units of Area

Unit	My Personal References
1 square inch (1 in^2)	
1 square foot (1 ft^2)	
1 square yard (1 yd^2)	
1 square centimeter (1 cm^2)	
1 square meter (1 m^2)	

Math Boxes 68

---

1. Complete the "What's My Rule?" table and state the rule.

Rule		in	out
		48	
		40	5
			$\frac{1}{8}$
			0
		16	

2. Tell the value of the following digits in 4,398,605.

a. 4 _____

b. 8 _____

c. 3 _____

d. 6 _____

e. 9 _____

---

3. Amanda found a can containing 237 dominoes. A full set has 28 dominoes. What is the greatest number of complete sets that can be in the can? _____

Explain how you found your answer. _____

_____

---

4. Tell whether each number is prime or composite.

a. Number of millimeters in 2.9 centimeters. _____

b. Number of inches in $1\frac{1}{2}$ yards. _____

c. Number of centimeters in 0.35 meter. _____

d. Number of feet in $4\frac{1}{3}$ yards. _____

e. Number of inches in $\frac{5}{6}$ foot. _____

---

5. Fill in the missing values on each number line.

a.

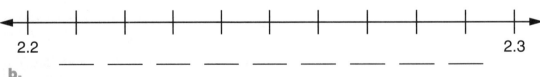

2.2   2.3

b.

6.93   7.03

Use with Lesson 68.

Finding the Areas of Nonrectangular Figures

In the previous lesson, you calculated the areas of rectangular figures using two different methods.

- You counted the total number of unit squares and parts of unit squares that fit neatly inside the figure.

- You used the formula $A = b * h$, where the letter A stands for *area*, the letter b for the length of the base, and the letter h for the *height*.

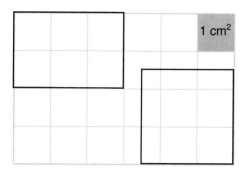

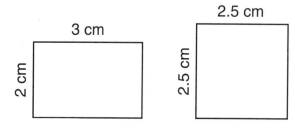

However, many times you will need to find the area of a figure that is not a rectangle. Unit squares will not fit neatly inside the figure, and you won't be able to use the formula for the area of a rectangle.

Working with a partner, think of a way to find the area of each of the figures below.

1. What is the area of triangle *ABC*?

   _____

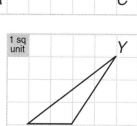

2. What is the area of triangle *XYZ*?

   _____

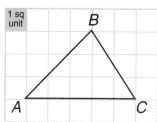

3. What is the area of parallelogram *GRAM*?

   _____

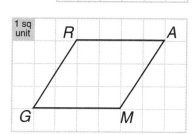

The Rectangle Method of Finding Area

Example A:

What is the area of triangle *ABC*?

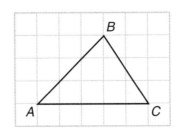

1. Find the areas of the two shaded parts. Add the two areas.

2. Draw a rectangle around the left shaded part. The area of the rectangle is 9 square units. The shaded area is $4\frac{1}{2}$ square units.

3. Draw a rectangle around the right shaded part. The area of the rectangle is 6 square units. The shaded area is 3 square units.

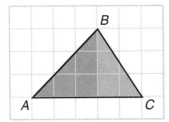

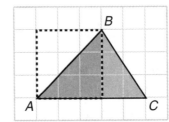

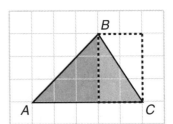

The area of triangle *ABC* is $4\frac{1}{2}$ + 3, or $7\frac{1}{2}$ square units.

Example B:

What is the area of triangle *XYZ*?

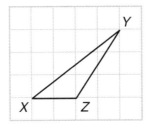

1. Draw a rectangle around the triangle. Find the area of rectangle *XRYS*. Subtract the two shaded areas.

2. The area of rectangle *XRYS* is 12 square units. The area of the darkly shaded triangle is 6 square units.

3. Draw a rectangle around the lightly shaded triangle. The area of the rectangle is 6 square units. The area of the triangle is 3 square units.

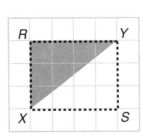

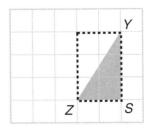

The area of triangle *XYZ* is 12 − 6 − 3, or 3 square units.

276

Finding Areas of Triangles and Parallelograms

Use the rectangle method to find the area of each triangle and parallelogram below.

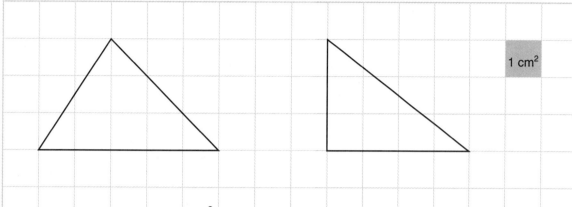

1. Area = _____ cm²   **2.** Area = _____ cm²

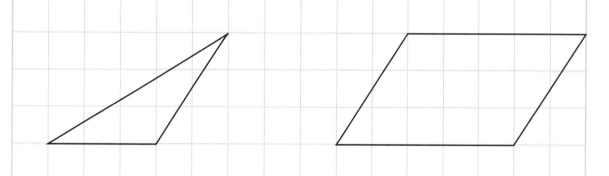

3. Area = _____ cm²   **4.** Area = _____ cm²

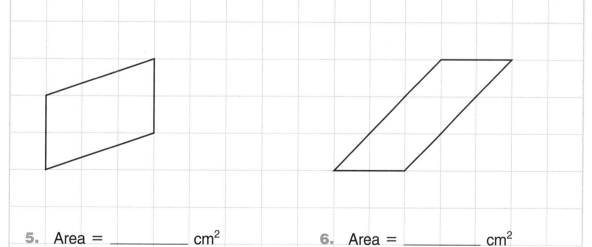

5. Area = _____ cm²   **6.** Area = _____ cm²

Math Message: Defining *Base* and *Height*

Study the figures below. Then write definitions for the words **base** and **height**.

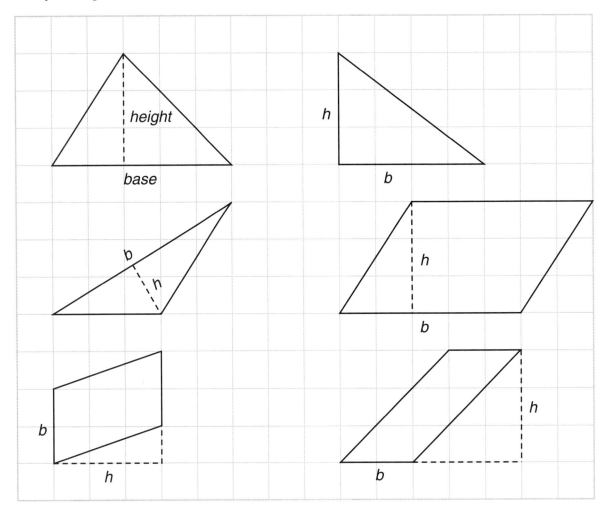

base:

_____

_____

height:

_____

_____

Math Boxes 69

---

1. During the last game, Eric ran the football six times. Following are the results for each run.

    1st run   +20 yards
    2nd run −6 yards
    3rd run   −5 yards
    4th run +10 yards
    5th run   −15 yards
    6th run   −9 yards

a. Did Eric end the game with a net gain or a net loss of yardage? _____

b. How much of a gain or loss? _____

---

2. Draw a rectangle whose perimeter is the same as the perimeter of the rectangle shown but whose sides do not have the same lengths.

         3.5 cm

2.5 cm ☐

3. What is the diameter of the largest circle that will fit inside the box for this problem?

_____

Explain your answer. _____

_____

_____

_____

---

4. Divide.

  a. 784 ÷ 16 = _____

  b. 613 ÷ 27 → _____

  c. 254 ÷ 54 → _____

  d. 979 ÷ 32 → _____

  e. 803 ÷ 37 → _____

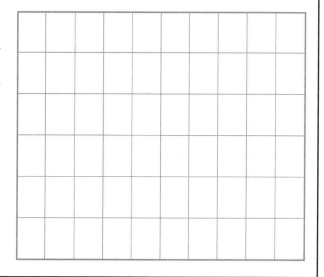

Finding Areas of Triangles and Parallelograms

1. Fill in the table. All figures are shown on page 281.

Figure	Area	Length of Base	Height	Length of Base * Height
Triangles				
A	3 cm²	3 cm	2 cm	6 cm²
B	_____ cm²	_____ cm	_____ cm	_____ cm²
C	_____ cm²	_____ cm	_____ cm	_____ cm²
D	_____ cm²	_____ cm	_____ cm	_____ cm²
E	_____ cm²	3 cm	4 cm	_____ cm²
F	_____ cm²	_____ cm	_____ cm	_____ cm²
Parallelograms				
G	6 cm²	3 cm	2 cm	6 cm²
H	_____ cm²	_____ cm	_____ cm	_____ cm²
I	_____ cm²	_____ cm	2 cm	_____ cm²
J	_____ cm²	_____ cm	_____ cm	_____ cm²

2. Examine the results of Figures A–F. Propose a formula for the area of a triangle as an equation and as a word sentence. Discuss it with others.

   Area of a triangle = _____

   _____

3. Examine the results of Figures G–J. Propose a formula for the area of a parallelogram as an equation and as a word sentence. Discuss it with others.

   Area of a parallelogram = _____

   _____

Using the Rectangle Method

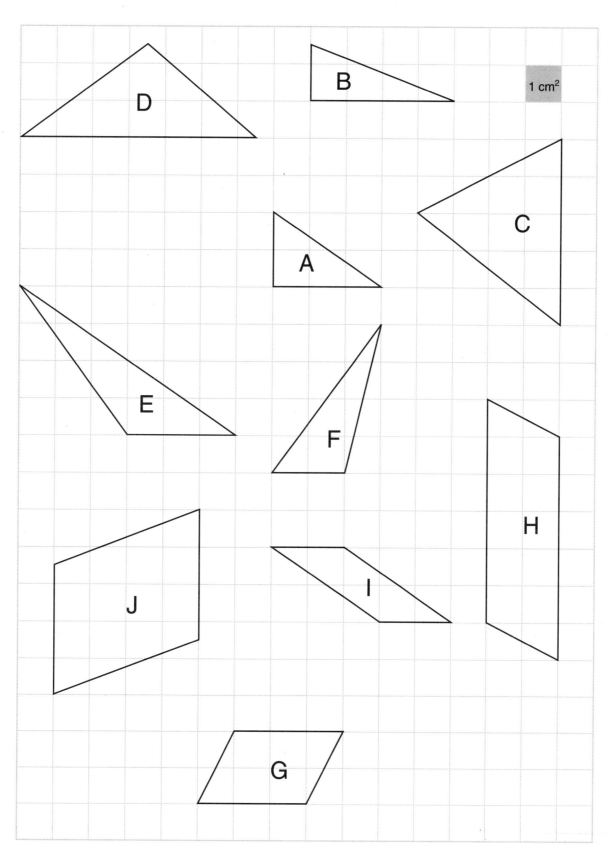

The Four-4s Problem

Using only four 4s and any operation on your calculator, create expressions for values from 1 through 100. Do not use any other numbers except for the ones listed in the rules below. You do not need to find an expression for every number. Some are quite difficult. Try to find as many as you can today, but keep working when you have free time. The rules are listed below:

- You must use four 4s in every expression.
- You can use two 4s to create 44 or three 4s to create 444.
- You may use 4^0. ($4^0 = 1$)
- You may use $\sqrt{4}$. ($\sqrt{4} = 2$)
- You may use 4! (four factorial). ($4! = 4 * 3 * 2 * 1 = 24$)

Use parentheses as needed so that it is very clear what is to be done and in what order. Examples of expressions for some numbers are shown below.

1 = _____   18 = _____

2 = _____   19 = _____

3 = _____   20 = _____

4 = _____   21 = _____

5 = _____   22 = _____

6 = _____   23 = _____

7 = _____   24 = _____

8 = _____   25 = _____

$9 = 4 + \sqrt{4} + \sqrt{4} + 4^0$ $26 = (4! + \sqrt{4}) * \frac{4}{4}$

10 = _____   27 = _____

11 = _____   28 = _____

12 = _____   29 = _____

13 = _____   30 = _____

14 = _____   31 = _____

15 = _____   32 = _____

16 = _____   33 = _____

17 = _____   34 = _____

The Four-4s Problem (continued)

35 = _____

36 = _____

37 = _____

38 = _____

39 = _____

40 = _____

41 = _____

42 = _____

43 = _____

44 = _____

45 = _____

46 = _____

47 = _____

48 = _____

49 = _____

50 = _____

51 = _____

52 = _____

53 = _____

54 = _____

55 = _____

56 = _____

57 = _____

58 = $(\sqrt{4} * (4! + 4)) + \sqrt{4}$

59 = _____

60 = _____

61 = _____

62 = _____

63 = _____

64 = _____

65 = _____

66 = _____

67 = _____

68 = _____

69 = _____

70 = _____

71 = _____

72 = _____

73 = _____

74 = _____

75 = _____

76 = _____

77 = _____

78 = _____

79 = _____

80 = _____

81 = _____

82 = _____

83 = _____

84 = _____

Use with Lesson 69.

The Four-4s Problem (continued)

85 = _____   93 = _____

86 = _____   94 = _____

87 = _____   95 = _____

88 = _____   96 = _____

89 = _____   97 = _____

90 = _____   98 = _____

91 = _____   99 = _____

92 = _____   100 = _____

_____

Math Message: Finding Areas of Polygons

Problem:

Find the area of triangle *ABC* without measuring its sides.

Solution:

Find the area of surrounding rectangle *AXYZ*.
Then subtract the areas of triangles 1, 2, and 3.

Area of rectangle *AXYZ* = 9 square units.
    Area of triangle 1 = 1 square unit.
    Area of triangle 2 = 3 square units.
    Area of triangle 3 = $1\frac{1}{2}$ square units.

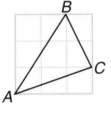

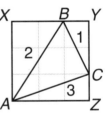

Area of triangle *ABC* = $9 - 1 - 3 - 1\frac{1}{2} = 3\frac{1}{2}$ square units.

Use the rectangle method to find the areas of the pentagon and triangle below.

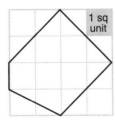

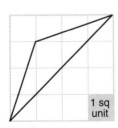

1 sq unit

1 sq unit

Area = _____ square units   Area = _____ square units

Finding Areas of Polygons with Standard Methods

Use any method you want to find the area of each polygon below. Record the area in the table on the right. You can use different methods with different figures. If you use any area formulas, be sure to remember that *height* is always measured perpendicular to the *base* you choose. Measure *base* and *height* very carefully.

Figure	Area
A	about _____ cm²
B	about _____ cm²
C	about _____ cm²
D	about _____ cm²
E	about _____ cm²
F	about _____ cm²

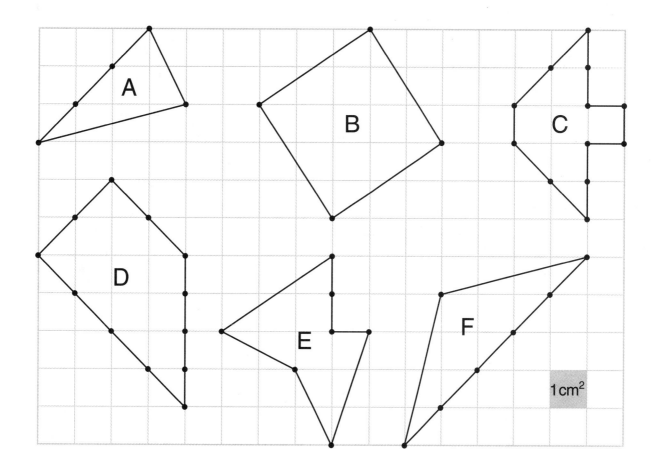

1 cm²

Finding Areas of Polygons with Pick's Formula

Read the paragraphs below and then use Pick's Formula to find the areas of
the polygons on the previous page. Record them in the table below. Compare them
to your results recorded in the table on the previous page. You should expect some
differences—measures are always estimates.

Pick's Formula for Finding Polygon Areas by Counting

In 1899 Georg Pick, an Austrian mathematician, discovered a formula for finding
the area of a polygon drawn on a square grid (such as graph paper). If a
polygon has its vertices at grid points, the area can be estimated very closely
by counting the number of grid points on the polygon (P) and the number of
grid points in the interior of the polygon (I) and then using the following formula
$A = (\frac{1}{2} * P) + I - 1$. The unit of area is the area of one square on the grid.

For figure B on the previous page,
the unit of area is cm^2.

$P = 4$ (grid points on polygon)
$I = 12$ (grid points in interior)
$A = (\frac{1}{2} * P) + I - 1$

$\quad = (\frac{1}{2} * 4) + 12 - 1$
$\quad = 13\ cm^2$

Figure	P	I	$A = (\frac{1}{2} * P) + I - 1$
A			about _____ cm^2
B			about _____ cm^2
C			about _____ cm^2
D			about _____ cm^2
E			about _____ cm^2
F			about _____ cm^2

Draw two polygons. Be sure that
vertices are at grid points. Use Pick's Formula to find the areas of the polygons.

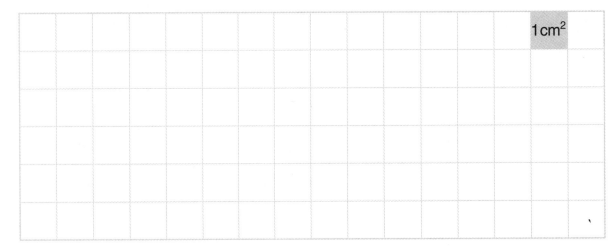

1cm²

Area: _____   Area: _____

Math Boxes 70

1. Use the grid on the right to locate the following objects on the map. The first one has been done for you.

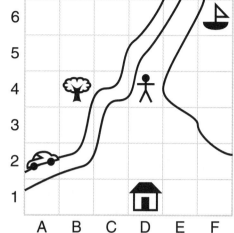

   a. fifth grader ___*D4*___

   b. boat _____

   c. car _____

   d. house _____

   e. tree _____

---

2. Circle the fractions and mixed numbers that are greater than 3.5.

   $2\frac{3}{8}$ $\frac{36}{9}$ $1\frac{7}{2}$ $\frac{24}{7}$ $3\frac{5}{12}$

---

3. Complete the table.

Standard Notation	Scientific Notation
300	$3 * 10^2$
3000	$3 * 10^3$
4000	
500	
	$7 * 10^3$

---

4. Multiply.

   a. $429 * 15 =$ _____

   b. $82 * 134 =$ _____

   c. _____ $= 706 * 189$

   d. _____ $= 214 * 48$

   e. _____ $= 591 * 73$

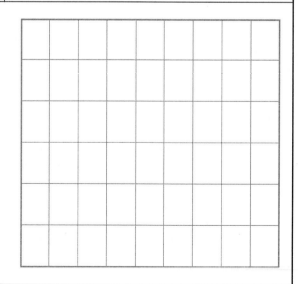

Date   Time

Perimeter of Enlarged/Reduced Shapes

Measure the sides of each polygon below to the nearest centimeter. Write measurements on the figure. Then calculate the perimeter.

1.

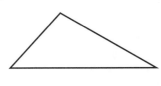

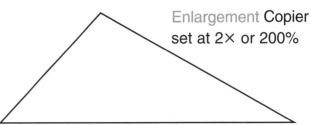

Enlargement **Copier**
set at 2× or 200%

The perimeter is about _____ cm.   The perimeter is about _____ cm.

2.

Reduction **Copier**
set at $\frac{1}{3}$× or 33%

The perimeter is about _____ cm.   The perimeter is about _____ cm.

3.

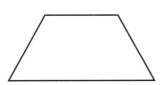

Enlargement
Copier set at
1.5× or 150%

The perimeter is about _____ cm.   The perimeter is about _____ cm.

4.

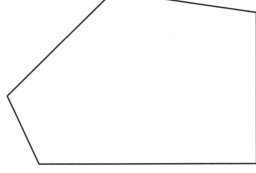

Reduction **Copier**
set at $\frac{1}{2}$× or 50%

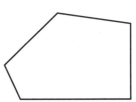

The perimeter is about _____ cm.   The perimeter is about _____ cm.

Perimeter of Enlarged/Reduced Shapes (continued)

Some copy machines let you reduce or enlarge what you are copying. To double every length on the original page, you set the machine at 2× or 200%. To reduce every length to $\frac{1}{2}$ that of the original, you set the machine at $\frac{1}{2}$× or 0.5× or 50%. Just as in enlarging or reducing photographs, every length in any direction is enlarged or reduced, which makes the final figure **similar** to the original figure— it looks the same but is larger or smaller.

5. Describe what happens to the sides and the perimeter of a figure in these situations:

   a. Copier says 2× or 200% _____

   _____

   _____

   b. Copier says $\frac{1}{2}$× or 50% _____

   _____

   _____

   c. Copier says 1.5× or 150% _____

   _____

   _____

   d. Copier says 3× or 300% _____

   _____

   _____

6. Use your protractor to measure the angles of the polygons on the previous page.

   Compare the angles of each original polygon to the angles of its enlargement or reduction.

   What happens to the angles of a figure when the figure is enlarged or reduced?

   _____

   _____

   _____

Area of Enlarged/Reduced Shapes

Measure the base and height of each polygon below to the nearest centimeter.
Write the measurements on the figure. Then calculate the area.

1.

Enlargement **Copier**
set at 2× or 200%

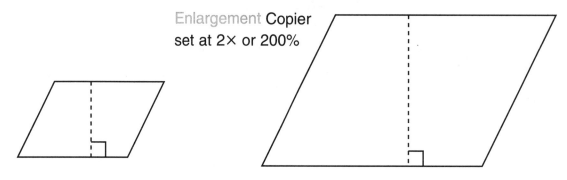

The area is about _____ cm².   The area is about _____ cm².

2.

Enlargement **Copier**
set at 3× or 300%

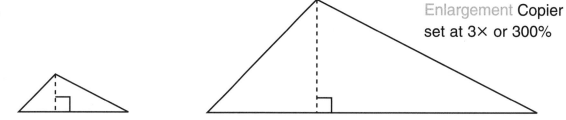

The area is about _____ cm².   The area is about _____ cm².

3.

Reduction **Copier**
set at $\frac{1}{2}$× or 50%

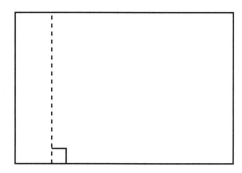

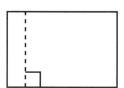

The area is about _____ cm².   The area is about _____ cm².

       Use with Lesson 71.

Area of Enlarged/Reduced Shapes (continued)

4. Describe what happens to the base, height, and area of a figure in these situations:

Copier Setting	Base	Height	Area
2× or 200%	_____	_____	_____
3× or 300%	_____	_____	_____
$\frac{1}{2}$× or 50%	_____	_____	_____
1.5× or 150%	_____	_____	_____

5. How are changes in perimeter different from changes in area when a figure is enlarged or reduced?

_____

_____

_____

_____

_____

_____

_____

_____

_____

_____

_____

_____

Use with Lesson 71.

Perimeter Patterns

Complete the tables below. Remember, perimeter is the distance around the *outside* of the figure. Use your Geometry Template to draw more polygons if you need help. Describe each pattern with words. For a challenge, describe the pattern with variables.

1.

 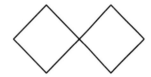

Polygons	1	2	3	4	5	10			100
Perimeter	3	4					22	50	

Describe the pattern: _____

_____

2.

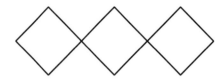

Polygons	1	2	3	4	5	10		25	
Perimeter	4	8					68		160

Describe the pattern: _____

_____

3.

 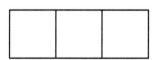

Polygons	1	2	3	4	5	10	25		100
Perimeter	4	6						68	

Describe the pattern: _____

_____

Perimeter Patterns (continued)

4.

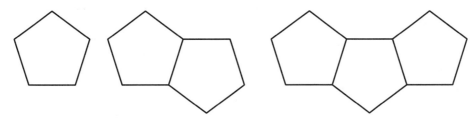

Polygons	1	2	3	4	5	10	20		100
Perimeter								143	

Describe the pattern: _____

_____

5. Use your Geometry Template to draw a perimeter pattern of your own below. Put two more numbers in the table—one in the top row and one in the bottom row. Exchange journals with your partner and complete each other's tables.

Polygons	1	2	3	4	5	10	20		
Perimeter									

Describe the pattern: _____

_____

Math Boxes 71

---

1. Javier has $5.00 to buy school supplies. He wants one pack of pencils for $1.38, a notebook for $2.74, and some fancy writing paper for $1.29 a pack. Does he have enough money?

_____

Explain your answer.

_____

_____

2. Divide mentally.

  a. $472 \div 5 \rightarrow$ _____

  b. $384 \div 6 =$ _____

  c. $729 \div 8 \rightarrow$ _____

  d. $543 \div 4 \rightarrow$ _____

  e. $576 \div 9 =$ _____

---

3. Complete the table.

Standard Notation	Exponential Notation
10,000	
	10^3
	10^8
1,000,000,000	
	10^5

4. Insert parentheses to make each sentence true.

  a. $19 + 41 * 3 = 180$

  b. $5 = 16 / 2 + 2 - 5$

  c. $-1 = 16 / 2 + 2 - 5$

  d. $24 \div 8 + 4 * 3 = 6$

  e. $24 \div 8 + 4 * 3 = 15$

---

5. Use fraction sticks to add the fractions.

  a. $\frac{1}{4} + \frac{1}{12} =$ _____

  b. $\frac{1}{3} + \frac{1}{12} =$ _____

  c. $\frac{1}{12} + \frac{2}{4} =$ _____

  d. $\frac{1}{12} + \frac{2}{3} =$ _____

  e. $\frac{1}{3} + \frac{1}{4} =$ _____

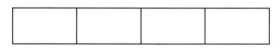

Use with Lesson 71.

Math Message: A Problem from the National Assessment

The following problem was in the mathematics section of the 1975 National Assessment of Educational Progress.

A square has a perimeter of 12 inches.
What is the area of the square?

Your answer: _____ in^2

The table below gives the national results for this problem.

	13-Year-Olds	17-Year-Olds	Young Adults
Correct answer	7%	28%	27%
144 sq inches	12%	19%	25%
48 sq inches	20%	10%	10%
24 sq inches	6%	4%	2%
12 sq inches	4%	3%	3%
6 sq inches	4%	2%	1%
3 sq inches	3%	2%	2%
Other incorrect answers	16%	13%	10%
No answer or "I don't know"	28%	19%	20%

Many students gave the answer 144 square inches or 48 square inches. Be prepared to discuss why you think they came up with those answers.

Ratio of Circumference to Diameter

You are going to explore the relationship between the circumference and the diameter of a circle.

1. Using a metric tape measure, carefully measure the circumference and diameter of a variety of round objects. Measure to the nearest millimeter (one-tenth of a centimeter).

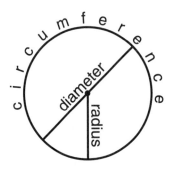

2. Fill in the first three columns of the table below.

Object	Circumference (C)	Diameter (D)	Ratio of Circumference to Diameter	
			Fraction Ratio (C/D)	Decimal Value (from calculator)
coffee cup	255 mm	80 mm	255/80	3.19
	mm	mm		
	mm	mm		
	mm	mm		
	mm	mm		
	mm	mm		

3. The students in your class combined their results in a stem-and-leaf plot. Use that plot to find the median value for the ratio C/D.

_____

The Value of π

Measurements are *always* estimates. But if we could measure round objects exactly, the ratio of the circumference to the diameter would be the same for every circle.

The ratio of the circumference of a circle to its diameter is called "**pi**" and is written as the Greek letter π.

Since ancient times, mathematicians have worked to find the value of π, just as you do today. Here are some of the earliest results. (*Note: c.* means *about.*)

Date	Source	Approximate Value of π
c. 1800–1650 B.C.	Babylonians	$3\frac{1}{8}$
c. 1650 B.C.	Rhind Papyrus (Egypt)	3.16
c. 950 B.C.	Bible (I Kings 7:23)	3
c. 240 B.C.	Archimedes (Greece)	Between $3\frac{10}{71}$ and $3\frac{1}{7}$
c. 470 A.D.	Tsu Ch'ungChi (China)	$\frac{355}{113}$ (3.1415929...) correct to 6 decimal places
c. 510 A.D.	Aryabhata (India)	$\frac{62,832}{20,000}$ (3.1416) less than 0.0001 different from π
c. 800 A.D.	al'Khwarizmi (Persia)	3.1416

In recent times, computers have been used to calculate the value of π. In 1949, π was calculated to 37,000 decimal places on ENIAC, one of the first computers. Later, π was computed to 100,000 digits on an IBM 7090 computer, and in 1981 to 2 million digits on a NEC supercomputer. In the years that followed, these calculations were extended to 17.5 million digits, then to 34 million digits, then to past 200 million digits, and in 1989 to more than 1 billion digits!

It's not possible to write π exactly with digits, because the decimal for π goes on forever. No pattern has ever been found in this decimal.

$$\pi = 3.14159265358979323846264338327950288419716939937751...$$

The Value of π (continued)

The number π is so important that most scientific calculators have a π key.

Press the π key on your calculator and record the display below.

_____ . _____ _____ _____ _____ _____ _____ _____ _____ _____

If you use the π key on your calculator, be sure to round your results. Results shouldn't be more precise than the original measurements. One or two decimal places are usually enough.

If you don't have a calculator with you, you can use an approximation for π. Since few measures are estimated more precisely than to hundredths, an approximation like 3.14 or $\frac{22}{7}$ is usually close enough.

Example: A circle has a diameter of 5 inches. What is its circumference?

Method 1: Use the π key on your calculator.

$C = \pi * D$

$C = \pi * 5 \text{ in} = 15.70796327 \text{ in}$

Method 2: Use 3.14 as an approximation for π.

$C = \pi * D$

$C = 3.14 * 5 \text{ in} = 15.7 \text{ in}$

Depending on how precise you think the 5-inch measurement is, round this result to 16 in, 15.7 in, or 15.71 in.

What a Memory!

In April 1995, the Xinhua News Agency in southern China reported that Zhang Zhuo, a 12-year-old boy, set a record by reciting the value of pi from memory to 4000 decimal places. He needed 25 minutes 30 seconds to accomplish this amazing feat. His error rate was 0.2 percent.

His performance broke the previous record of 1000 digits set by another Chinese boy many years ago.

Math Boxes 72

1. Complete the "What's My Rule?" table and state the rule.

Rule	in	out
	5	
	3	−2
		5
	0	
		−7

2. Write a number story for 185 ÷ 6 and solve it.

_____

_____

_____

Answer: _____

3. Mr. Carroll's class collected autumn leaves and sorted them by color. The class had 24 yellow leaves, 17 green leaves, 37 red leaves, 8 orange leaves, and 14 brown leaves. Make a circle graph of the data.

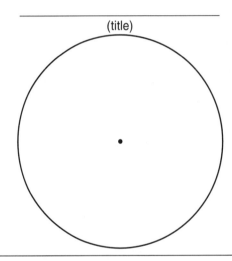
(title)

4. What is the measure of ∠A?

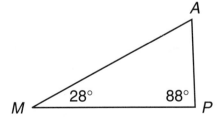

The measure of ∠A is _____°.

5. Round each number to the nearest hundredth.

a. 432.089 _____

b. 650.1 _____

c. 227.715 _____

d. 38.207 _____

e. 61.099 _____

The Rectangular Land Survey System

The Rectangular Land Survey System was adopted by the Continental Congress in 1784. The map at the right shows the area that the U.S. General Land Office has surveyed since then.

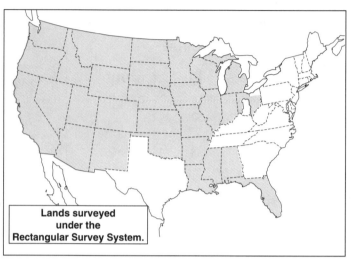

Lands surveyed under the Rectangular Survey System.

Lands were surveyed before they were transferred from the government to private ownership. The surveyors used reference lines parallel to the east/west parallels of latitude and the north/south meridians of longitude to divide the land. The survey is called a **rectangular system** because the reference lines outline pieces of land shaped almost like rectangles.

Note: Earth is shaped almost like a sphere. As you travel north, meridians of longitude get closer together, and parallels of latitude get shorter. So the figures formed by reference lines are not quite rectangles or squares.

The reference lines form **townships** that are 6 miles on each side (36 square miles). Each township is divided into 36 small **sections** that are 1 mile on each side (1 square mile).

Measuring Land in Acres

Within sections, land in the United States is usually measured in acres.

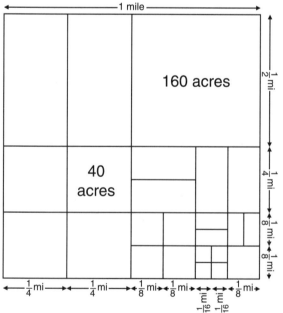

The **acre** originally meant a large piece of useful farmland. During medieval times, an acre was the amount of land a man could plow in one day with a pair of oxen. By the 1400s, an acre was defined as 43,560 square feet.

An acre can be any shape. It does not need to be a square. It does not even need to be a rectangle.

A football field, excluding the end zones, is slightly larger than 1 acre.

There are exactly 640 acres in 1 square mile.

How Big Is an Acre?

Reference

1 square foot: about 1.5 pages of this journal
1 square yard: about 14 pages of this journal
1 square meter: about 17 pages of this journal
1 acre: about 67,000 pages of this journal
                   about 1 football field (excluding
                      the end zones)

1 acre = 43,560 square feet
1 square mile = 640 acres

For a rectangle:
$A = b * h$

For a triangle:
$A = \frac{1}{2} * b * h$

1. Use your calculator to find the area and perimeter of each figure.

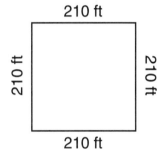

210 ft
210 ft   210 ft
210 ft

Area = _____

Perimeter = _____

Is the area larger than, smaller than, or about equal to 1 acre?

_____

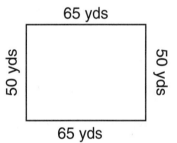

65 yds
50 yds   50 yds
65 yds

Area = _____

Perimeter = _____

Is the area larger than, smaller than, or about equal to 1 acre?

_____

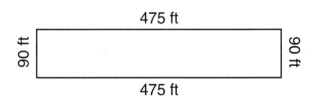

475 ft
90 ft   90 ft
475 ft

Area = _____

Perimeter = _____

Is the area much larger than, much smaller than, or about equal to 1 acre?

_____

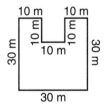

10 m   10 m
10 m   10 m
30 m   10 m   30 m
30 m

Area = _____

Perimeter = _____

Is the area much larger than, much smaller than, or about equal to 1 acre?

_____

How Big Is an Acre? (continued)

Do NOT use your calculator for the problems on this page. (You really don't need it!)

2. Find the area and perimeter of the figure on the right.

Area = _____

Perimeter = _____

Is the area much larger than, much smaller than, or about equal to 1 acre?

_____

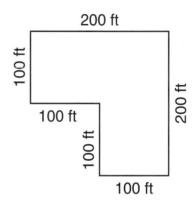

3. Find the area and perimeter of this triangular piece of land.

Area = _____

Perimeter = _____

Is the area much larger than, much smaller than, or about equal to 1 acre?

_____

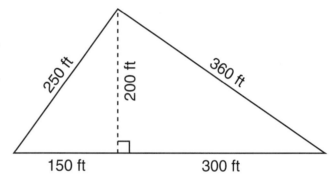

4. The figure on the right shows a 1-square-mile city area. A rectangular system of streets divides the area into city blocks.

Each block is a square with $\frac{1}{8}$-mile sides.

Which has a larger area, 1 block or 1 acre? _____

What is the area of 1 block, in acres? _____

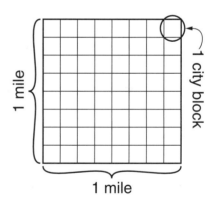

Math Boxes 73

1. On the map, draw each animal whose location is given below.

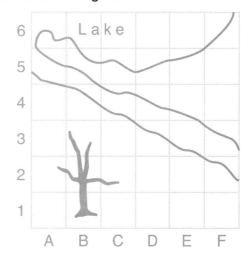

   a. a bird in C2

   b. a fish in D6

   c. a turtle in E3

   d. a snake in F1

   e. a frog in F4

2. Circle the fractions and mixed numbers that are less than 3.5.

$$-\frac{7}{2} \qquad \frac{18}{4} \qquad 2\frac{5}{3} \qquad \frac{29}{8} \qquad 3\frac{4}{9}$$

3. Complete the table.

Standard Notation	Scientific Notation
8000	$8 * 10^3$
60,000	
	$5 * 10^5$
	$4 * 10^6$
700,000	

4. Solve.

   a.   43   **b.**   75   **c.**   425
      * 191   * 88   * 68

   d.   759   **e.**   422   **f.**   648
      * 13   * 185   * 92

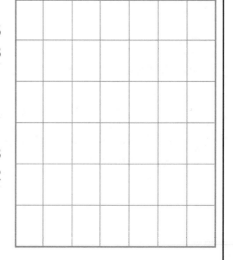

Math Message: Representing Fractions as Decimals

Reference
1 foot = 12 inches
1 quart = 2 pints
1 gallon = 4 quarts = 8 pints

Part 1

a. What fraction of 1 foot is 6 inches? _____ ft

Write that fraction as a decimal. _____ ft

b. What fraction of 1 foot is 3 inches? _____ ft

Write that fraction as a decimal. _____ ft

c. What fraction of 1 foot is 4 inches? _____ ft

Write that fraction as a decimal. _____ ft

Part 2

a. What fraction of 1 gallon is 2 pints? _____ gal

Write that fraction as a decimal. _____ gal

b. What fraction of 1 gallon is 7 pints? _____ gal

Write that fraction as a decimal. _____ gal

Part 3

a. Write 3 feet 6 inches as a decimal. _____ ft

b. Write 7 feet 3 inches as a decimal. _____ ft

c. Write 4 gallons 6 pints as a decimal. _____ gal

d. How would you write 2 gallons 3 pints
as a decimal? _____ gal

Use with Lesson 74.

Playing Areas for Combat Sports

Use your calculator to find
each playing area.

Scale:

1 mm (drawing)
represents 1 ft (actual).

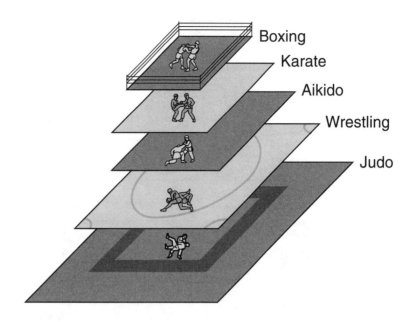

Sport	Dimensions	Playing Area
Boxing	20 ft by 20 ft	ft^2
Karate	26 ft by 26 ft	ft^2
Aikido	29 ft 6 in by 29 ft 6 in*	ft^2
Wrestling	39 ft 3 in by 39 ft 3 in*	ft^2
Judo	52 ft 6 in by 52 ft 6 in*	ft^2

*Calculate with decimals. For example, 29 ft 6 in is equal to 29.5 ft.

Source: COMPARISONS by the Diagram Group. Reprinted by permission of St. Martin's Press.

Playing Areas for Other Sports

Use your calculator to find each playing area.
Circle "more" or "less" to tell whether each
area is more or less than 1 acre.

1 acre = 43,560 square feet

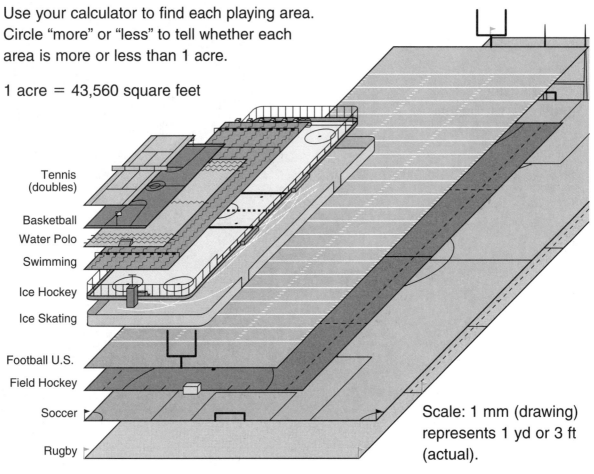

Scale: 1 mm (drawing) represents 1 yd or 3 ft (actual).

Sport	Dimensions	Playing Area	More or Less than 1 Acre?	
Tennis (doubles)	78 ft by 36 ft	ft²	more	less
Basketball	94 ft by 50 ft	ft²	more	less
Water Polo	98 ft by 65 ft	ft²	more	less
Swimming	165 ft by 69 ft	ft²	more	less
Ice Hockey	200 ft by 85 ft	ft²	more	less
Ice Skating	200 ft by 100 ft	ft²	more	less
Football (U.S.)	300 ft by 160 ft*	ft²	more	less
Field Hockey	300 ft by 180 ft	ft²	more	less
Soccer	360 ft by 240 ft	ft²	more	less
Rugby	472 ft by 226 ft	ft²	more	less

*Not including end zones

Source: COMPARISONS by the Diagram Group. Reprinted by permission of St. Martin's Press.

Math Boxes 74

1. Julie makes $4.00 per week for doing the dishes every night of the week. She paid her sister $0.75 each time she did the dishes for her. Is that a fair price? Explain your answer.

_____

_____

_____

_____

2. Divide mentally.

a. 829 ÷ 4 → _____

b. 608 ÷ 3 → _____

c. 943 ÷ 2 → _____

d. 780 ÷ 5 = _____

e. 698 ÷ 7 → _____

3. Complete the table.

Exponential Notation	Product of Factors	Standard Notation
10^2		
	10 * 10 * 10 * 10	
		10,000,000
10^8		
	10 * 10 * 10 * 10 * 10 * 10	

4. Insert parentheses to make each sentence true.

a. 48 ÷ 6 + 2 * 4 = 16

b. 48 ÷ 6 + 2 * 4 = 24

c. 45 = 54 − 24 / 6 − 5

d. 0 = 54 − 24 / 6 − 5

e. 30 = 54 − 24 / 6 − 5

5. Add the fractions.

a. $\frac{1}{3} + \frac{1}{6} =$ _____

b. $\frac{3}{6} + \frac{1}{3} =$ _____

c. $\frac{2}{3} + \frac{2}{12} =$ _____

d. $\frac{5}{6} + \frac{1}{12} =$ _____

e. $\frac{1}{2} + \frac{1}{3} =$ _____

Math Message: Estimate the Area of a Circle

Use the circle at the right to solve
Problems 1–4.

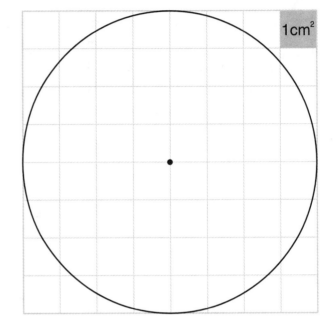

1cm²

1. Estimate the area of this
    circle by counting squares.

    about _____ cm²

2. The diameter of the circle is

    about _____ cm.

3. The radius of the circle is about

    _____ cm.

4. The circumference of the circle is about _____ cm.

Follow-up

5. What is the median of all the area estimates in your class? _____ cm²

More Pi, Anyone?
In 1997, two Japanese computer scientists claimed a
new world record when they calculated pi to more than
51,539,600,000 digits on a computer at the University of
Tokyo. The work took 29 hours to do and 37 hours to check.
If a number with that many digits were printed in one line
with 6 digits per centimeter, it would stretch more than
85,000 kilometers, or twice around Earth at the equator.
Source: University of Tokyo.

Inscribing a Square in a Circle

A polygon is said to be **inscribed** in a circle if all its vertices are on the circle.

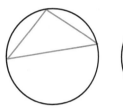

1. Using your compass and straightedge only, construct an inscribed square in a circle *with a diameter of 8 centimeters*. Use the pictures below to guide you.

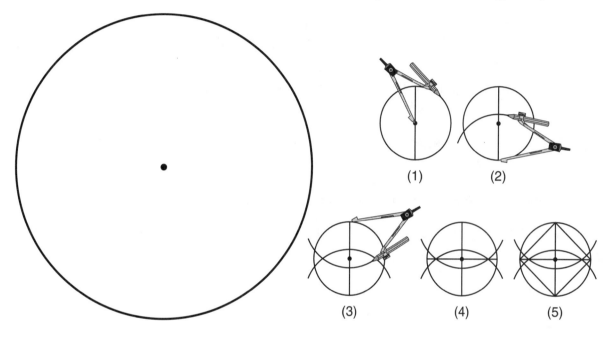

(1) (2) (3) (4) (5)

2. What is the area of the inscribed square? _____ cm²

   (*Hint:* Use your ruler to measure the sides.)

3. Is the area of the inscribed square more or less than the area of the circle? _____

4. Which is a better approximation for the true area of the circle—the area of the inscribed square or the estimate you made by counting squares? Why?

   _____

   _____

   _____

Inscribing a Regular Hexagon in a Circle

1. Inscribe a regular hexagon in a circle, as follows.

   Step 1: On the grid below, draw a circle with center at point *C* and a diameter of 8 centimeters. Keep the same compass opening for Steps 2 and 3.

   Step 2: Place the anchor of your compass on point *A* and make a mark with the pencil point on the circle.

   Step 3: Place the anchor of your compass on the mark you just made and make another mark with the pencil point on the circle. Do this four more times so that your marks divide the circle into 6 equal parts. The sixth mark should be on or near point *A*.

   Step 4: With your straightedge, connect the 6 marks on the circle to form a regular hexagon.

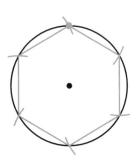

2. What is the area of the inscribed hexagon? _____ cm²

   (*Hint:* Think of the hexagon as being made up of 6 identical triangles. Find the area of one triangle and use that to find the area of the entire hexagon.)

3. Is the area of the inscribed hexagon more or less than the area of the circle? _____

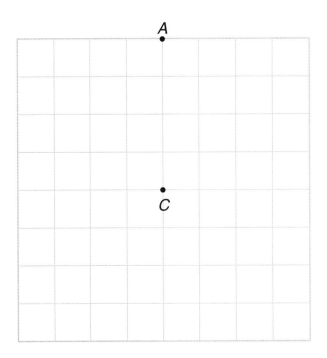

Use with Lesson 75.

A Formula for the Area of a Circle

There is a formula for the area of a circle, just as there are formulas for the area of a rectangle, triangle, and parallelogram and a formula for the area of a polygon with vertices at grid points (Pick's Formula).

> **The formula for the area of a circle is**
>
> $$A = \pi * r^2$$
>
> where A is the area of a circle and r is the radius of the circle.

Use this formula to calculate the area of a circle with a diameter of 8 centimeters.

The area of the circle is about _____ cm².

Answer the following questions. Be prepared to discuss your answers with your class.

1. a. Which of your three previous estimates is the
      best approximation for the true area of the circle? _____

   b. How far is this estimate from the actual area?   _____

2. a. Which of your estimates is the least accurate
      for the true area of the circle?   _____

   b. Why do you think this is so?

   _____

3. Name an inscribed figure that would be a
   better approximation for the area of the circle
   than a hexagon.   _____

4. Do you think the area of an inscribed triangle would be a good approximation
   for the area of a circle? Explain your answer.

   _____

   _____

   _____

Can Your Body Pass through an Index Card?

1. Fold a 5-inch by 8-inch index card down the middle "widthwise." (The fold is along the 5-inch width of the card.)

2. Hold the halves of the folded card together. Cut the card as shown by the lines in Diagram A. Some cuts start at the fold and go almost to the edge of the card. Some cuts start at the edge and go almost to the fold. Be sure the first and last cuts start at the fold. Cuts should alternate between starting at the fold and starting at the edge.

3. Open the card. Cut along the fold from X to Y as shown in Diagram B. Be careful not to cut to the edges of the card.

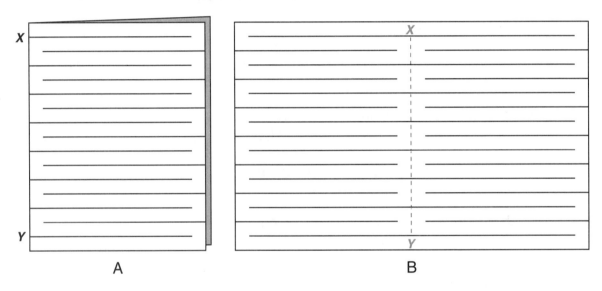

A   B

4. Pull the card apart carefully. You'll have a paper ring. Is it large enough for your body to pass through?

Challenge

Using another 5-inch by 8-inch index card, how can you cut out a ring that has a perimeter twice the perimeter of the ring you just made?

_____

_____

_____

Math Boxes 75

1. Complete the "What's My Rule?" table and state the rule.

Rule	in	out
	2	−10
		0
	16	4
	3	
		−5

2. Write a number story for 385 ÷ 25 and solve it.

_____

_____

_____

Answer: _____

3. Ms. Barrie's fifth graders collected information on favorite board games. Complete the table, and make a circle graph of the data.

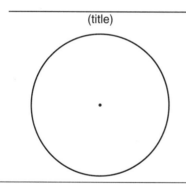

_____
(title)

Favorite Games	Number of Students	Percent of Class
Monopoly®	18	
Risk®	8	
Life®	6	
Stratego®	6	
Clue®	12	
Total		

4. What are the measures of ∠1 and ∠2?

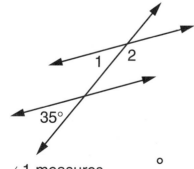

∠1 measures _____°.

∠2 measures _____°.

5. Round each number to the nearest thousand.

a. 456,823 _____

b. 711,809 _____

c. 2,400,657 _____

d. 7,594,621 _____

e. 7,052 _____

Time to Reflect

1. Imagine that you and a friend are playing a game. You are thinking of the word *mathematics*. You can give your friend 10 clues to help guess this word. Each clue must be one word long, and the clues may not contain any part of the word *mathematics*. What 10 words will you use?

1. _____   6. _____

2. _____   7. _____

3. _____   8. _____

4. _____   9. _____

5. _____   10. _____

2. If you and a friend got different answers to a math problem, what would you do?

_____

_____

_____

_____

_____

_____

_____

_____

_____

_____

_____

_____

_____

314

Math Boxes 76

1. **a.** Plot the following points on the grid:
(4,2); (2,4); (2,7); (6,7)

   b. Connect the points with line
segments in the order given above.
Then connect (6,7) and (4,2).
What shape have you drawn?

_____

_____

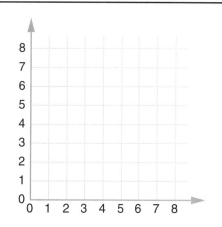

2. Find the perimeter and area for each figure below.

Rectangle	Triangle	Parallelogram
$A = b * h$	$A = \frac{1}{2} * b * h$	$A = b * h$

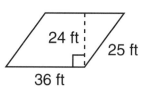

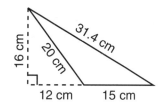

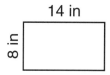

Perimeter: _____   Perimeter: _____   Perimeter: _____

Area: _____   Area: _____   Area: _____

3. **a.** What is the diameter of a circle
if its radius is 4 cm?

> $Area = \pi * r^2$
> $Circumference = 2 * \pi * r$

Radius: _4 cm_ Diameter: _____

   b. Find the area and circumference
of the circle. Round the area to
the nearest square centimeter
and the circumference to the
nearest centimeter.

Area: _____   Circumference: _____

4. Tell whether you would find the
circumference (*C*), perimeter (*P*),
or area (*A*) in each situation.

   a. Measure the amount of
fencing needed to enclose
a triangular garden.

_____

   b. Estimate the size of the
plastic needed to cover
the ground under a
backyard swimming pool.

_____

Math Message: Comparing and Ordering Numbers

For any pair of numbers on the number line, the number to the left is less than the number to the right.

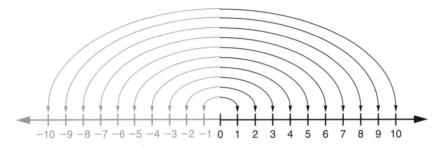

−10 is less than −5, because −10 is to the left of −5.
We use the **less than** symbol (<) to write −10 < −5.

+10 is greater than −5, because +10 is to the right of −5.
We use the **greater than** symbol (>) to write +10 > −5.

Reminder

When writing the > or < symbol, be sure
the arrow tip points to the smaller number.

---

1. Write > or <.

   −5 _____ 5   10 _____ −10   −10 _____ 0

   14 _____ 7   −14 _____ −7   0 _____ −6$\frac{1}{2}$

2. List the numbers in order from least to greatest.

   −10, 14, −100, $\frac{8}{2}$, −17, 0 _____

   −0.5, 0, −4, π, −4.5 _____

3. Name four positive numbers less than π. _____

   Name four negative numbers greater than −π. _____

Using Counters to Show an Account Balance

Tear out Activity Sheet 16 from the back of your journal. Shade the ⊞ squares with a regular pencil and the ⊟ squares with a red pencil or crayon. Then cut out the squares.

Each ⊞ counter represents $1 of cash on hand.

Each ⊟ counter represents a $1 IOU (I Owe You), or debt.

Your **account balance** is the amount of money either that you have or that you owe. If you have money in your account, your balance is **"in the black."** If you owe money, your account is **"in the red."**

1. Suppose you have this set of counters.   ⊞ ⊞ ⊞ ⊞ ⊞ ⊟ ⊟ ⊟

    What is your account balance?   _____

    Are you "in the red" or "in the black"?   _____

2. Use ⊞ and ⊟ counters to show an account with a balance of +$5. Draw a picture of the counters below.

3. Use ⊞ and ⊟ counters to show an account with a balance of −$8. Draw a picture of the counters below.

4. Use ⊞ and ⊟ counters to show an account with a balance of $0. Draw a picture of the counters below.

Addition of Positive and Negative Numbers

1. Use your counters to help you solve these problems.

   Draw ⊞ and ⊟ counters to show how you solved each problem.

   a. $+8 + (-2) =$ _____

   b. $-4 + (-5) =$ _____

   c. $-3 + (+7) =$ _____

2. Solve these addition problems.

   a. $50 + (-30) =$ _____   b. _____ $= -50 + 30$

   c. $-16 + 10 =$ _____   d. _____ $= 16 + (-10)$

   e. $-9 + (-20) =$ _____   f. _____ $= -15 + 15$

   g. $27 + (-18) =$ _____   h. _____ $= -43 + (-62)$

   i. $-17 + (-17) =$ _____   j. _____ $= -55 + 32$

Math Boxes 77

---

1. List the factors of 142.

   _____

2. Write the following numbers in order, from greatest to least:

   $0.98,$ $\frac{15}{14},$ $\frac{9}{10},$ $1\frac{1}{6},$ 0.8

   _____

   _____

   _____

   _____

   _____

---

3. Divide.

   a. $597 \div 12 \rightarrow$ _____

   b. $3840 \div 22 \rightarrow$ _____

   c. $1630 \div 15 \rightarrow$ _____

   d. $8289 \div 27 =$ _____

   e. $4761 \div 31 \rightarrow$ _____

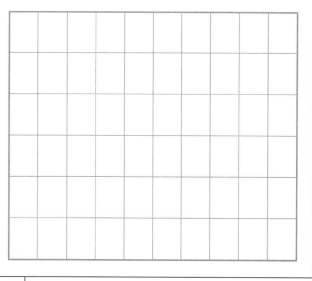

---

4. a. Write the smallest number you can make that is less than 1 by using each of the following digits only once: 8 9 2 3 0

   _____

   b. Write this number in words.

   _____

   _____

   _____

5. Find something in the room that is about 18 inches long.

   _____

Estimation Challenge: Area

What Is the Ground Area of Your School?

What is the ground area of your school? In other words, what area of land is taken up by the ground floor?

Work alone or with a partner to come up with an estimation plan. How can you estimate the ground area of your school without measuring it with a tape measure? Discuss your ideas with your classmates.

My estimation plan:

_____

_____

_____

_____

_____

_____

_____

_____

My best estimate:

_____

_____

How accurate is your estimate? What range of areas might the actual area fall in?

_____

_____

_____

_____

320   Use with Lesson 78.

Quick Division with Single Digits

Review this strategy for solving division problems with one-digit divisors:

Example 1:   364/7 = ?

Break up 364 into two or more "friendly" numbers, each of which is easily divisible by 7. Make one of the numbers an extended 7s fact. For example:

Break up 364:	364 = 350 + 14
Divide each part:	350/7 = 50 and 14/7 = 2
Add the results:	50 + 2
Solution:	364/7 = 50 + 2 = 52

Example 2:   297/8 = ?

Break up 297:	297 = 240 + 57
Divide each part:	240/8 = 30 and 57/8 → 7 R1
Add the results:	30 + 7 R1
Solution:	297/8 → 37 R1

Example 3:   727/4 = ?

Break up 727:	727 = 400 + 320 + 7
Divide each part:	400/4 = 100 and 320/4 = 80 and 7/4 → 1 R3
Add the results:	100 + 80 + 1 R3
Solution:	727/4 → 181 R3

Break each dividend into "friendly" numbers. Then complete the division for each part of the problem and record the answer.

1.   129/3 = ?

129 = _____

129/3 = _____

2.   375/5 = ?

375 = _____

375/5 = _____

3.   477/9 = ?

477 = _____

477/9 = _____

4.   649/4 = ?

649 = _____

649/4 → _____

Math Boxes 78

1. Use fraction sticks to add the fractions. Do not use a calculator.

   a. $\frac{1}{4} + \frac{3}{3} =$ _____

   b. $\frac{1}{8} + \frac{1}{2} =$ _____

   c. $\frac{5}{8} + \frac{1}{4} =$ _____

   d. $\frac{5}{12} + \frac{1}{4} =$ _____

   e. $\frac{3}{4} + \frac{1}{12} =$ _____

2. Find the area of the rectangle.

   | Area of a rectangle = $b * h$ |
   --- |

   14 cm

   8 cm

   Area: _____

3. Round each number to the nearest hundred thousand.

   a. 1,576,023 _____

   b. 24,703,998 _____

   c. 654,327 _____

   d. 8,219,540 _____

   e. 61,349,999 _____

4. Circle the numbers below that are evenly divisible by 6. Do not use a calculator.

   148   293   762   1050   984

5. **a.** Measure the radius of the circle in centimeters. _____

    b. Find the area to the nearest square centimeter and the circumference to the nearest centimeter.

    | Area = $\pi * radius^2$ |
    --- |
    | Circumference = $\pi * diameter$ |

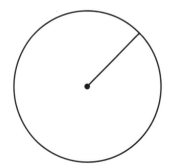

    The area is about _____.

    The circumference is about _____.

Math Message: Subtracting Numbers

The containers shown below contain ⊞ and ⊟ counters. Each ⊞ counter represents $1 of cash on hand. Each ⊟ counter represents a $1 IOU, or debt. The balance for any container is the total value of the combined cash and IOU counters.

Example: A container holds 50 ⊞ counters and 35 ⊟ counters. The balance is 15 ⊞ counters, or $15 in cash.

1. Balance = _____

30⊞   10⊟

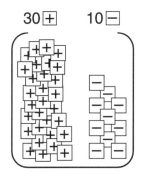

If 22 ⊟ counters are added to the container, what is the new balance?

Balance = _____

2. Balance = _____

10⊞   20⊟

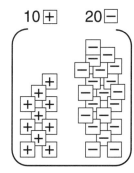

If 16 ⊟ counters are subtracted from the container, what is the new balance?

Balance = _____

3. Balance = _____

30⊞   10⊟

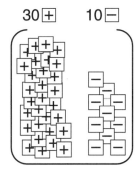

If 22 ⊞ counters are subtracted from the container, what is the new balance?

Balance = _____

4. Balance = _____

10⊞   20⊟

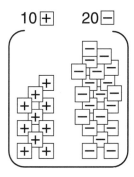

If 16 ⊞ counters are added to the container, what is the new balance?

Balance = _____

Subtracting Numbers (continued)

5. Work with a partner. At first, you and your partner will answer different sets of questions.

   Decide who is Student 1 and who is Student 2. Then each student:

   - places 10 [+] and 10 [−] counters on his or her desk.
   - completes the transactions listed in his or her table on page 325.
   - records the new balance in the "Balance" column in the table after each move.

   Leave the "Number Model" column blank.

6. When you have both completed all 6 transactions in your table, record your partner's results in the other table. Compare your results.

   In what ways are the tables alike?

   ____

   ____

   ____

   In what ways do the tables differ?

   ____

   ____

   ____

   Wait for instructions from your teacher.

7. Fill in the "Number Model" column in both tables.

8. Write a rule for subtracting positive and negative numbers.

   ____

   ____

   ____

   ____

   ____

Subtracting Numbers (continued)

Table 1

Student 1:

Transaction	Balance	Number Model
Start.	*0*	
1. Subtract 2 ⊞.	*2* ⊟	
2. Add 4 ⊟.		
3. Add 6 ⊞.		
4. Subtract 5 ⊟.		
5. Subtract 4 ⊞.		
6. Add 3 ⊞.		

Table 2

Student 2:

Transaction	Balance	Number Model
Start.	*0*	
1. Add 2 ⊟.	*2* ⊟	
2. Subtract 4 ⊞.		
3. Subtract 6 ⊟.		
4. Add 5 ⊞.		
5. Add 4 ⊟.		
6. Subtract 3 ⊟.		

Subtraction Problems

Rewrite each subtraction problem as an addition problem. Then solve it.

1. $100 - 45 =$ _____ *100 + (−45)* _____ = _____

2. $-100 - 45 =$ _____ = _____

3. $160 - (-80) =$ _____ = _____

4. $9 - (-2) =$ _____ = _____

5. $-4 - (-2) =$ _____ = _____

6. $-15 - (-30) =$ _____ = _____

7. $8 - 10 =$ _____ = _____

8. $-20 - (-7) =$ _____ = _____

9. $\pi - (-\pi) =$ _____ = _____

10. $0 - (-6.1) =$ _____ = _____

Number Stories

11.   Jody believes that her basketball team will win its next game by 12 points.

   a.   If the team wins by 5 points, did she overestimate
        or underestimate the difference in the final score?   _____

        By how many points?   _____

   b.   If the team wins by 14 points, did she overestimate
        or underestimate the difference in the final score?   _____

        By how many points?   _____

12.   A city has two suburban airports, Airport A and Airport B.
      The temperature at Airport A is usually about 3°F cooler
      than the temperature in the city. The temperature at
      Airport B is usually about 5°F cooler than the temperature
      at Airport A. If the temperature in the city is −13°F, what
      is the temperature at Airport B?   _____

326   Use with Lesson 79.

Math Boxes 79

---

1. Name two equivalent fractions for each fraction below.

a. $\frac{7}{8}$ = _____

b. $\frac{3}{10}$ = _____

c. $\frac{6}{7}$ = _____

d. $\frac{1}{6}$ = _____

e. $\frac{12}{5}$ = _____

2. Measure line segment AB to the nearest $\frac{1}{4}$ inch.

A •———————————————• B

_____

3. a. Plot the following points on the coordinate grid.

$(-3, -3); (1, 1); (4, 1); (0, -3)$

b. Connect the points with line segments in the order given above. Then connect $(-3, -3)$ and $(0, -3)$.

What shape have you drawn?

_____

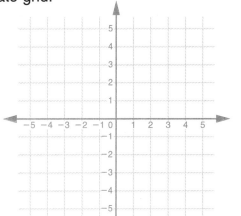

4. Draw the next picture in each pattern.

a.

b.

Math Message

1. Find each sum or difference.

 a. $18 - (+10) = $ _____ $18 - 10 = $ _____ $18 + (-10) = $ _____

 b. $-7 + (-4) = $ _____ $-7 - (+4) = $ _____ $-7 - 4 = $ _____

Slide-Rule Problems

Example 1: Addition	Example 2: Subtraction
$-3 + 6 = ?$	$-6 - 4 = ?$
1. Align the 0-mark on the slider with -3 on the holder.	1. Align the 0-mark on the slider with -6 on the holder.
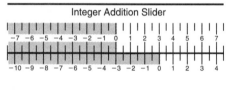	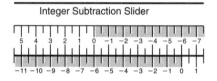
2. Find 6 on the slider. It is aligned with 3 on the holder. This is the answer to the problem.	2. Find 4 on the slider. It is aligned with -10 on the holder. This is the answer to the problem.
$-3 + 6 = 3$	$-6 - 4 = -10$

2. Use your slide rule to solve each problem.

 a. $12 - 17 = $ _____   **b.** $12 + (-17) = $ _____

 c. $10 - (-4) = $ _____   **d.** $10 + 4 = $ _____

 e. $-10 - (-5) = $ _____   **f.** $19 - 2.5 = $ _____

 g. $-2 + (-13) = $ _____   **h.** $-7.5 + 18 = $ _____

 i. $9 + $ _____ $= -9$ **j.** $3 - $ _____ $= -16$

 k. _____ $- 5 = -8$ **l.** $-1.25 + (-11.25) = $ _____

Math Boxes 80

1. List the factors of 165.

_____

2. Write the following numbers in order, from greatest to least.

2.14 $\frac{9}{4}$ 11/5 $2\frac{1}{8}$ 2.3

_____

_____

_____

_____

_____

3. Divide.

a. $2935 \div 17 \rightarrow$ _____

b. $8796 \div 43 \rightarrow$ _____

c. $1515 \div 76 \rightarrow$ _____

d. $384 \div 21 \rightarrow$ _____

e. $6207 \div 97 \rightarrow$ _____

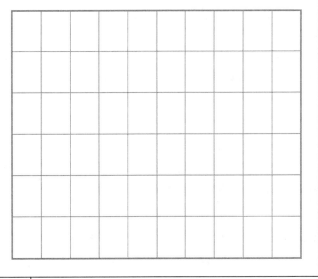

4. **a.** Write the largest number you can that is less than 1 by using each of the following digits only once: 4 7 5 2 0

_____

b. Write this number in words.

_____

_____

_____

5. Find something in the room that is about 18 centimeters long.

_____

How Do You Enter a Negative Number in the Calculator?

1. **a.** Enter the number 3 in your calculator. Then press
   the [+⇆] key. What number is shown in the display?   _____

   b. What happens if you keep pressing the [+⇆] key? _____

   _____

   _____

2. Repeat the steps in Problem 1 with other numbers.

3. **a.** What is the opposite of 5?
   Enter the opposite of 5 in the calculator.   _____

   b. What is the opposite of the opposite of 5?
   Enter this number in the calculator, using the [+⇆] key.   _____

4. What does the [+⇆] key do? _____

   _____

   _____

Addition and Subtraction on the Calculator

Study the following examples. Then solve the problems on page 331.

Example 1: $6 + (-4) = ?$

   Solution: Enter 6, [+], 4, [+⇆], [=]   Answer: 2

Example 2: $6 - (-2) = ?$

   Solution: Enter 6, [−], 2, [+⇆], [=]   Answer: 8

Example 3: $-6 - (-2) = ?$

   Solution: Enter 6, [+⇆], [−], 2, [+⇆], [=]   Answer: −4

Addition and Subtraction on the Calculator (continued)

1. Use your calculator to solve each problem. Record how you did it.

   Example: **Calculator Entries**

   $12 + (-17) =$ _____ -5 _____   _____ *12, [+], 17, [+⟳-], [=]* _____

   a. $-10 - 17 =$ _____   _____

   b. $-10 + (-17) =$ _____   _____

   c. $-27 + 220 =$ _____   _____

   d. $19 - 43 =$ _____   _____

   e. $-35 - (-35) =$ _____   _____

   f. $72 + (-47) =$ _____   _____

2. Solve. Use your calculator.

   a. $3.65 - 2.02 =$ _____

   b. $10 - (-5) =$ _____

   c. $-901 - 199 =$ _____

   d. $-7.1 + 18.6 =$ _____

   e. $888 - 456 =$ _____

   f. $11.25 - 3 =$ _____

   g. $-2 + (-13) + 7 =$ _____

   h. $2 - 7 - (-15) =$ _____

   i. $41 / 328 =$ _____

   j. $3 * \pi =$ _____

   k. $-(41 / 328) =$ _____

   l. $-(3 * \pi) =$ _____

   m. $41 * (7 + 2) =$ _____

   n. $41 * (7 + (-2)) =$ _____

Penny Weights

The materials out of which a penny is made were changed at the beginning of one of these years: 1981, 1982, or 1983. As a result, the weight of a penny has changed. Your task to is find out in what year the weight of pennies changed.

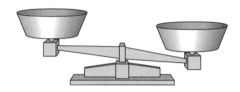

1. Compare 1981 pennies to 1982 pennies.
   Put ten 1981 pennies in one pan and ten 1982 pennies in the other pan.

   Do the pans balance? _____

2. Return the pennies to their correct containers.
   Put ten 1982 pennies in one pan and ten 1983 pennies in the other pan.

   Do the pans balance? _____

3. I think that penny weights changed beginning in the year _____,

   because _____

   _____

Number Stories

4. A salesperson is often assigned a quota. A quota is the dollar value of goods that the salesperson is expected to sell.

   Suppose a salesperson is $3500 below quota and then makes
   a sale of $4700. Has the salesperson exceeded his or her quota? _____

   If yes, by how much? _____

5. A stock goes up $\frac{1}{4}$ dollar per share one day. The next day, it goes down $1\frac{1}{2}$ dollars. The third day, it goes up $3\frac{1}{4}$ dollars.

   Did the value of the stock increase or decrease after 3 days? _____

   By how much? _____

Use with Lesson 81.

Math Boxes 81

1. Use fraction sticks to add the fractions. Do not use a calculator.

a. $\frac{1}{3} + \frac{3}{6} =$ _____

b. $\frac{1}{3} + \frac{5}{9} =$ _____

c. $\frac{2}{9} + \frac{2}{3} =$ _____

d. $\frac{4}{12} + \frac{1}{9} =$ _____

e. $\frac{1}{3} + \frac{5}{12} =$ _____

2. Find the area of the rectangle.

$$\text{Area} = b * h$$

12 m

6 m

Area: _____

3. Round each number to the nearest ten thousand.

a.   4,032,654 _____

b.   67,959,821 _____

c.   17,008,342 _____

d. 785,298,055 _____

e.   63,864,923 _____

4. Circle the numbers below that are evenly divisible by 9. Do not use a calculator.

3735   2043   192   769   594

5. a. Draw a circle with a radius of 2.5 centimeters.

$$\text{Area} = \pi * r^2$$

b. What is the area of this circle to the nearest square centimeter?

about _____

Math Message: Land Elevation in the United States

1. Use the *American Tour Almanac* to find the highest and lowest point in the U.S. and its territories.

	Name	**State**	**Elevation**
Highest Point			
Lowest Point			

2. What is the difference in elevation between the highest point and the lowest point in the U.S. and its territories?   _____

3. About how many miles is this? (*Note:* 1 mile = 5280 feet)   _____

4. Fill in the table below for the elevation in your state or territory.

	Name	**Elevation**
Highest Point		
Lowest Point		

5. What is the difference in elevation between the highest point and the lowest point in your state or territory? (*Note:* The elevation of sea level is 0 feet.)   _____

6. Is the highest point in your state or territory more or less than 1 mile above sea level?   _____

Math Boxes 82

---

1. Name two equivalent fractions for each fraction below.

a. $\frac{4}{5} =$ _____

b. $\frac{5}{9} =$ _____

c. $\frac{3}{7} =$ _____

d. $\frac{6}{11} =$ _____

e. $\frac{8}{3} =$ _____

2. Measure line segment CD to the nearest $\frac{1}{16}$ inch.

C   D

_____

---

3. **a.** Plot the following points on the coordinate grid.

(−4,−1); (−3,1); (1,3); (2,1); (−2,−1)

b. Connect the points with line segments in the order given above. Then connect (−4,−1) and (−2,−1).

What shape have you drawn?

_____

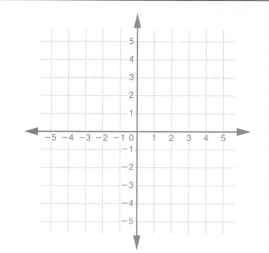

---

4. Draw the next picture in each pattern.

a.

b.

Land Elevation in the United States (continued)

Mile-High States

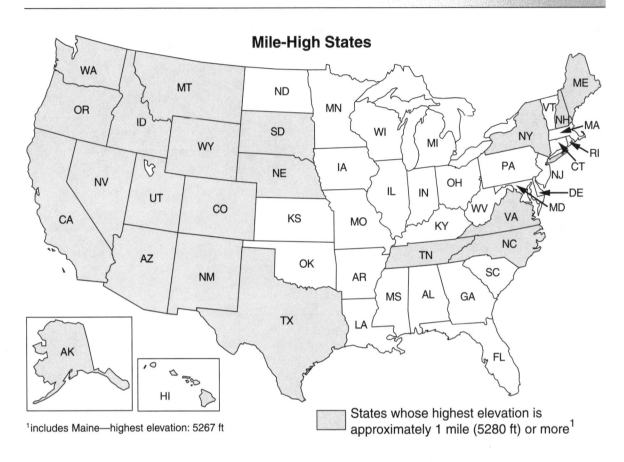

[1]includes Maine—highest elevation: 5267 ft

States whose highest elevation is approximately 1 mile (5280 ft) or more[1]

Very Cold States

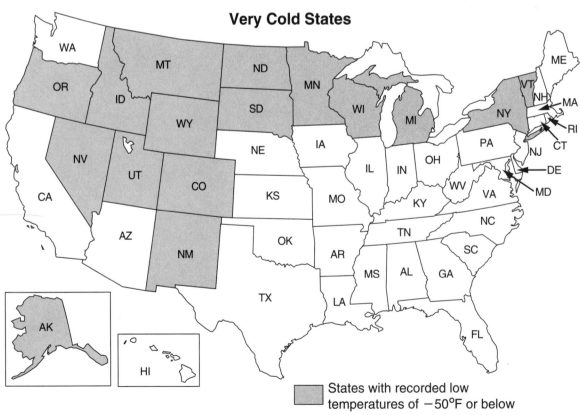

States with recorded low temperatures of −50°F or below

Use with Lesson 82.

Land Elevation in the United States (continued)

Use the maps on page 336 to answer the following questions:

1. Do all states with an elevation of at least 1 mile also have a recorded low temperature of −50°F or below?

   _____

2. Do all states with a low of −50°F or below also have elevations of at least 1 mile?

   _____

3. Which states with a low of −50°F or below do not have elevations of at least 1 mile?

   _____

Use the latitude and longitude map on the inside back cover of the *American Tour Almanac* to answer the following questions:

4. Are all states with a low of −50°F or below in the northern half of the United States? (Are they on or above 40 degrees north latitude?)

   _____

   Which state or states are not?

   _____

5. Do all states with a low of −50°F or below either fall in the northern half of the U.S. or have an elevation of at least 1 mile?

   _____

Absolutely, Kelvin!
There are temperature scales other than Celsius and Fahrenheit. The Kelvin scale, proposed by British physicist Lord Kelvin in 1848, is used by scientists. It begins at "absolute zero"—the coldest possible temperature, or −273.15°C. Absolute zero is called 0 kelvin. A kelvin is equal to 1 degree Celsius, so water freezes at 273.15 kelvin (0°C) and boils at 373.15 kelvin (100°C). The Rankine scale is similar but is based on degrees Fahrenheit.

Source: Britannica Online.

Population Map

Using the color-coded data map on page 24 of the *American Tour Almanac,* answer the following questions:

1. Are states with large areas estimated to have more 25- to 44-year-olds? Are states with small areas estimated to have fewer people of this age? Give at least two examples to support your answer.

_____

_____

_____

_____

2. Are the states that are expected to have fewer than 500,000 people who are 25 to 44 years old in 2020 scattered throughout the United States, or are they grouped together? Give examples to support your answer.

_____

_____

_____

_____

Challenge

3. What geographic feature do all the states expected to have 2 million or more 25- to 44-year-olds in 2020 have in common? (*Hint:* Refer to the map on pages 28–29 of the *American Tour Almanac.*)

_____

_____

_____

_____

Making a Color-Coded Data Map

To make a color-coded data map, you need to do the following:

- Find or calculate the data you want the map to display.

- Organize the data into categories.

- Assign a different color to each category and make a map legend.

- Color each state according to the map legend.

- Give the map a title.

Work with a partner. Select just one of Data Sets 1–4 below. If you wish, organize the data in a different way or find your own data in an almanac or other source. Make a color-coded data map using the map on journal page 341.

Then look for interesting patterns on your map and write a paragraph at the bottom of page 340 about what you found.

Data Set 1   *Topic:* Going to Work on Public Transportation

Data: Second column of the table on page 44 of the *American Tour Almanac*

Suggested Organization: Four categories for Percent of Workers Using Public Transportation
10.0% or more
5.0% to 9.9%
1.0% to 4.9%
Less than 1.0%

Data Set 2   *Topic:* Urban Population

Data: Page 46 of the *American Tour Almanac*

Suggested Organization: Four categories for Percent of Population in Urban Areas
80.0% or more
65.0% to 79.9%
50.0% to 64.9%
Less than 50.0%

Making a Color-Coded Data Map (continued)

Data Set 3　*Topic:* Forests

　　　　　　Data: Page 47 of the *American Tour Almanac*

　　　　　　Suggested Organization: Four categories for Estimated Percent
　　　　　　　　　　　　　　of Land That Is Forest
　　　　　　　　　　　　　　60% or more
　　　　　　　　　　　　　　40% to 59.9%
　　　　　　　　　　　　　　20% to 39.9%
　　　　　　　　　　　　　　Less than 20%

Data Set 4　*Topic:* Farmland

　　　　　　Data: Page 47 of the *American Tour Almanac*

　　　　　　Suggested Organization: Three categories for Estimated Percent
　　　　　　　　　　　　　　of Land That Is Farmland
　　　　　　　　　　　　　　60% or more
　　　　　　　　　　　　　　30% to 59.9%
　　　　　　　　　　　　　　Less than 30%

Write a paragraph about what you found.

_____

_____

_____

_____

_____

_____

_____

_____

_____

_____

340　　　　　　　　　　　　　　　　　　Use with Lesson 82.

Making a Color-Coded Data Map (continued)

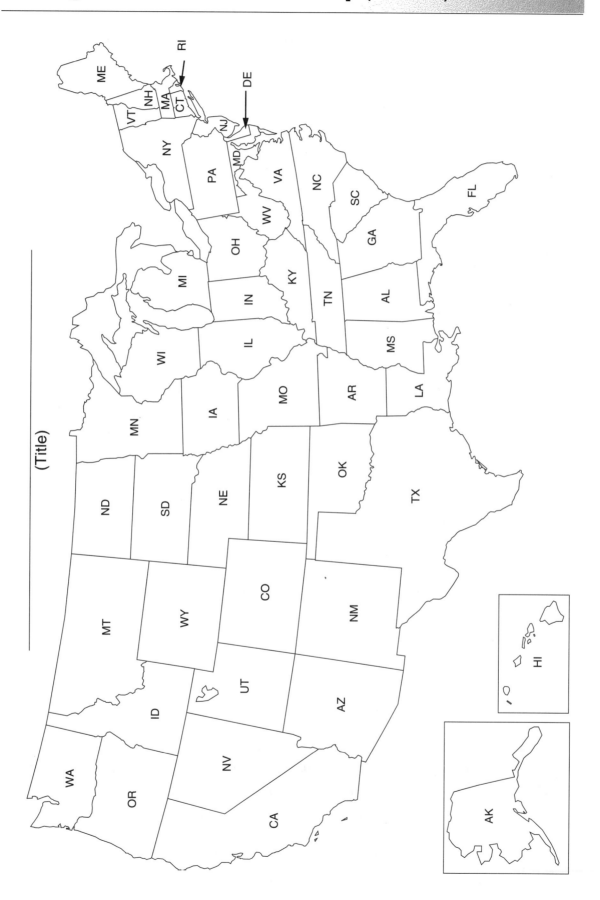

(Title)

Pan-Balance Equations

Solve these pan-balance problems. In each figure, the two pans are in perfect balance.

1. One cube weighs

   as much as _____ marbles.

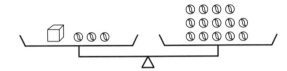

2. One cube weighs

   as much as _____ oranges.

3. One orange weighs

   as much as _____ grapes.

   (half orange)

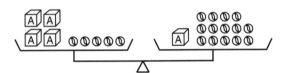

4. One block weighs

   as much as _____ marbles.

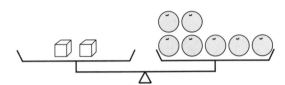

Check your answers:

The sum of the answers to Problems 1 and 2 should equal $14\frac{1}{2}$.

The sum of the answers to Problems 3 and 4 should equal 25.

Did You Know

Housing Boom
Some might say that Parker Brothers (the games company) has built more houses than any other developer in the world. Since 1935, the company has "built" more than 3 billion houses for its Monopoly® game.

Source: *Games* Magazine.

Pan-Balance Equations (continued)

Solve these pan-balance problems. In each figure, the two pans are in perfect balance.

5. One □ weighs

   as much as _____ △'s.

6. One □ weighs

   as much as _____ marbles.

   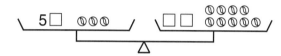

7. One x weighs

   as much as _____ balls.

Check your answers:

The sum of the answers to Problems 5 and 6 should equal 4.

The sum of the answers to Problems 6 and 7 should equal 5.

Challenge

8. An empty bottle weighs as much as 6 marbles.

   The contents of a full bottle weigh

   as much as _____ marbles.

   A full bottle weighs as

   much as _____ marbles.

   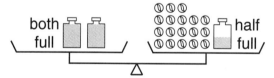

Math Boxes 83

---

1. Rename each fraction as a mixed number.

a. $\frac{28}{6} =$ _____

b. $\frac{34}{5} =$ _____

c. $\frac{19}{4} =$ _____

d. $\frac{24}{9} =$ _____

e. $\frac{43}{10} =$ _____

2. Multiply or divide mentally.

a. $386 \div 4 \rightarrow$ _____

b. $673 \div 9 \rightarrow$ _____

c. $68 * 50 =$ _____

d. $299 * 15 =$ _____

e. $295 \div 5 =$ _____

---

3. Complete the "What's My Rule?" table and state the rule.

Rule

in	out
8	
	2
2	−6
0	
	−9

4. Circle < or > to show whether the product is less than or greater than 10,000.

a. $93 * 95$ <   >   10,000

b. $5 * 751$ <   >   10,000

c. $885 * 15$ <   >   10,000

d. $200 * 800$ <   >   10,000

e. $300 * 300$ <   >   10,000

---

5. If the hexagon on your Geometry Template represents 3, what is the value of each shape below?

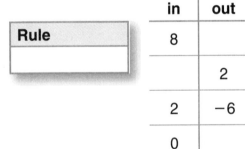

a. _____

b. _____

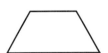

c. _____

d. _____

e. _____

Use with Lesson 83.

More Pan-Balance Equations

Solve these problems, using both pan balances in each problem. In each problem, the pans are in perfect balance. The weights of objects, such as blocks, balls, marbles, and coins, may be different from problem to problem but are consistent within each problem.

1. One block weighs

as much as _____ marbles.

One ball weighs

as much as _____ marbles.

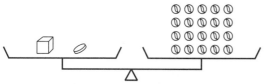

2. One block weighs

as much as _____ marbles.

One coin weighs

as much as _____ marbles.

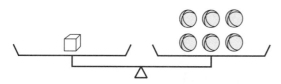

3. One block weighs

as much as _____ marbles.

One ball weighs

as much as _____ marbles.

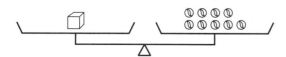
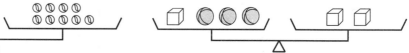

4. One block weighs

as much as _____ marbles.

One ball weighs

as much as _____ marbles.

More Pan-Balance Equations (continued)

Solve these pan-balance problems. In each figure, the two pans are in perfect balance.

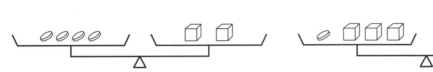 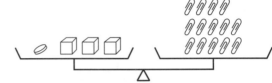

5. One coin weighs

as much as _____ clips.

One block weighs

as much as _____ clips.

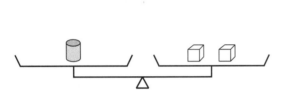 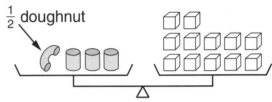

6. One can weighs

as much as _____ blocks.

One doughnut weighs

as much as _____ blocks.

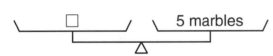 

7. One □ weighs

as much as _____ marbles.

One △ weighs

as much as _____ marbles.

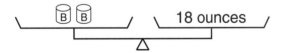 

8. Each can weighs B ounces.

B = _____

Each cube weighs A ounces.

A = _____

Use with Lesson 84.

More Pan-Balance Equations (continued)

Solve these pan-balance problems. In each figure, the two pans are in perfect balance.

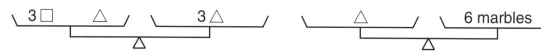

9. One ☐ weighs

   as much as _____ marbles.

One △ weighs

   as much as _____ marbles.

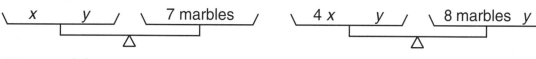

10. *y* weighs

   as much as _____ marbles.

x weighs

   as much as _____ marbles.

11. If the cup is full, **the coffee in the cup** weighs as much as _____ marbles.

   If the cup is full, **the coffee plus the cup** weighs as much as _____ marbles.

12. Two pens weigh as much as one compass. One pen and one compass together weigh 45 grams.

   Complete the pan-balance sketches below. Find the weight of one pen and of one compass.

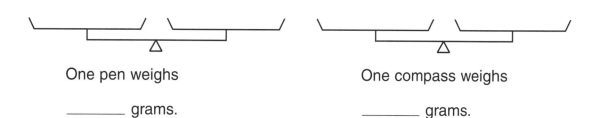

One pen weighs

_____ grams.

One compass weighs

_____ grams.

Math Boxes 84

1. Insert < or >.

a. $\frac{8}{9}$ _____ $\frac{8}{10}$

b. $\frac{3}{5}$ _____ $\frac{3}{7}$

c. $\frac{6}{7}$ _____ $\frac{5}{6}$

d. $\frac{7}{12}$ _____ $\frac{7}{14}$

e. $\frac{9}{11}$ _____ $\frac{14}{15}$

2. **a.** Circle any triangles that look like equilateral triangles.

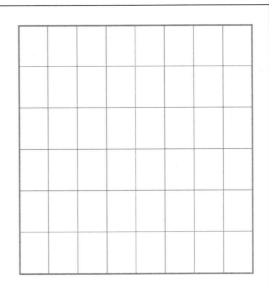

b. Write a definition of an equilateral triangle.

_____

_____

_____

3. Estimate the answer for each problem. Then solve each problem.

	Estimate	**Solution**
a. 603 * 71	_____	_____
b. 29 * 802	_____	_____
c. 48 × 202	_____	_____
d. 397 × 497	_____	_____
e. 22 * 550	_____	_____

4. **a.** Make a stem-and-leaf plot of the following numbers:

120, 111, 137, 144, 121, 120, 95, 87, 120, 110, 135, 90, 86, 143, 95

b. Find the landmarks.

Mode: _____

Median: _____

Range: _____

Stems (10s)	Leaves (1s)

Use with Lesson 84.

Algebraic Expressions

Variables are symbols—such as □, *X*, *x*, or *G*—which stand for a specific number that is not known.

Example: John gets a raise of $5 per week. What is his new weekly salary?

Because we don't know John's weekly salary before he got his raise, we can't tell what his new salary is. If we use the variable *s* to represent his old weekly salary, we can represent his new salary as *s* + 5.

s + 5 is an example of an **algebraic expression.** An algebraic expression uses operation symbols with variables, alone or with numbers.

Complete each statement below with an algebraic expression, using the suggested variable. The first problem has been done for you.

---

1. If Beth's allowance is $2.50 more than Ann's, then Beth's allowance is

   _____ *D* + $2.50 _____.

   Ann's allowance   Beth
   is *D* dollars.

---

2. If Ali's grandfather is 50 years older than Ali, then Ali is

   _____ years old.

   Ali's grandfather   Ali
   is *G* years old.

---

3. Seven baskets of potatoes weigh

   _____ pounds.

   A basket of potatoes
   weighs *P* pounds.

Algebraic Expressions (continued)

4. If a submarine dives 150 feet, then it will be traveling at a depth of

_____ feet.

A submarine is traveling at a depth of *X* feet.

5. The floor is divided up for gym classes into 5 equal-sized areas. Each class has a playing area of

_____ ft².

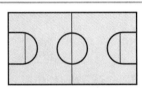

The gym floor has an area of *A* square feet.

6. The charge for a book that is *D* days overdue is

_____ cents.

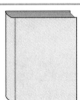

A library charges 10 cents for each overdue book. It adds an additional charge of 5 cents per day for each overdue book.

7. If Kevin spends $\frac{2}{3}$ of his allowance on a book, then he has

_____ dollars left.

Kevin's allowance is *X* dollars.

"What's My Rule?"

1. State in words the rule for the "What's My Rule?" table at the right.

   _____

   _____

   _____

   _____

   Circle the number sentence that describes the rule.

   $Y = X/5$ $Y = X - 4$ $X + Y = 4$

X	Y
5	1
4	0
−1	−5
1	−3
2	−2

2. State in words the rule for the "What's My Rule?" table at the right.

   _____

   _____

   _____

   _____

   Circle the number sentence that describes the rule.

   $Z - Q = 2$ $Z = 2 * Q$ $Z = \frac{1}{2}Q * 1$

Q	Z
1	3
3	5
−4	−2
−3	−1
−2.5	−0.5

3. State in words the rule for the "What's My Rule?" table at the right.

   _____

   _____

   _____

   _____

   Circle the number sentence that describes the rule.

   $g = 2 * t$ $t = 2 * g$ $t = 4 * g$

g	t
$\frac{1}{2}$	2
0	0
2.5	10
$\frac{1}{4}$	1
5	20

2-4-5-8-10 Frac-Tac-Toe

If you use a standard deck of playing cards:

- Use Queens as zeros (0).

- Use Aces as ones (1).

- Discard Jacks and Kings.

If you use an *Everything Math Deck,* discard cards greater than 10.

You can play with coins: One partner is "heads," and the other partner is "tails."

Or use a pencil to initial the squares. Print lightly so you can erase and use the game board again.

Numerator
Pile

All remaining
cards

Denominator
Pile

Two each
of 2, 4, 5, 8,
and 10 cards

> 1.0	0 or 1	> 2.0	0 or 1	> 1.0
0.2	0.3	0.25 or 0.75	0.4	0.5
> 1.5	0.125 or 0.375	0.375 or 0.625	0.625 or 0.875	> 1.5
0.5	0.6	0.25 or 0.75	0.7	0.8
> 1.0	0 or 1	> 2.0	0 or 1	> 1.0

Use with Lesson 85.

2-4-5-8-10 Frac-Tac-Toe

If you use a standard deck of playing cards:

- Use Queens as zeros (0).

- Use Aces as ones (1).

- Discard Jacks and Kings.

If you use an *Everything Math Deck,* discard cards greater than 10.

You can play with coins: One partner is "heads," and the other partner is "tails."

Or use a pencil to initial the squares. Print lightly so you can erase and use the game board again.

| Numerator Pile |
| All remaining cards |

| Denominator Pile |
| Two each of 2, 4, 5, 8, and 10 cards |

>100%	0% or 100%	>200%	0% or 100%	>100%
20%	30%	25% or 75%	40%	50%
>150%	$12\frac{1}{2}\%$ or $37\frac{1}{2}\%$	$37\frac{1}{2}\%$ or $62\frac{1}{2}\%$	$62\frac{1}{2}\%$ or $87\frac{1}{2}\%$	>150%
50%	60%	25% or 75%	70%	80%
>100%	0% or 100%	>200%	0% or 100%	>100%

Use with Lesson 85.

Math Boxes 85

---

1. Rename each mixed number as a fraction.

a. $2\frac{3}{8} =$ _____

b. $4\frac{4}{5} =$ _____

c. $3\frac{8}{3} =$ _____

d. $10\frac{2}{7} =$ _____

e. $5\frac{1}{9} =$ _____

2. Multiply or divide mentally.

a. $999 * 47 =$ _____

b. $250 * 12 =$ _____

c. $943 \div 7 \rightarrow$ _____

d. $784 \div 4 =$ _____

e. $599 * 30 =$ _____

---

3. Complete the "What's My Rule?" table and state the rule.

in	out
20	
	0
	-3
5	-5
1	

Rule: _____

4. Circle <, =, or > to show whether the quotient is less than, equal to, or greater than 100.

a. 700/70   <   =   >   100

b. 8000/10   <   =   >   100

c. 900/9   <   =   >   100

d. 1000/10   <   =   >   100

e. 100,000/100   <   =   >   100

---

5. If the trapezoid on your Geometry Template is worth 1, what is the value of each shape below?

Whole
trapezoid

a. _____

b. _____

c. _____

Use with Lesson 85.

Math Boxes 86

---

1. Insert < or >.

   a. $\frac{9}{14}$ _____ $\frac{10}{13}$

   b. $\frac{6}{21}$ _____ $\frac{2}{6}$

   c. $\frac{4}{11}$ _____ $\frac{7}{16}$

   d. $\frac{8}{18}$ _____ $\frac{3}{7}$

   e. $\frac{5}{24}$ _____ $\frac{2}{10}$

2. **a.** Draw an isosceles triangle.

   b. Write a definition of an isosceles triangle.

   _____

   _____

   _____

---

3. Estimate the answer for each problem. Then solve the problem.

	Estimate	Solution
a. 302 * 57	_____	_____
b. 599 × 9	_____	_____
c. 701 × 97	_____	_____
d. 18 × 403	_____	_____
e. 498 * 501	_____	_____

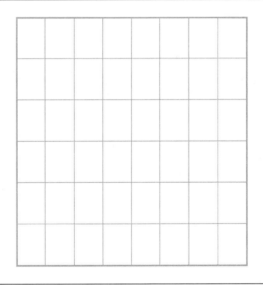

---

4. **a.** Make up a set of 15 numbers that has the following landmarks.

   Maximum: 152
   Range: 25
   Mode: 139
   Median: 142

Stems (10s)	Leaves (1s)

   b. Make a stem-and-leaf plot of the data.

Math Message: Travel in 1 Minute

A plane travels at a **speed** of 480 miles per hour. At that rate, how many miles will it travel in 1 minute? Write a number model to show what you did to solve the problem.

Number model: _____ Distance per minute: _____ miles

Speed

For an airplane flying at 8 miles per minute (480 mph), you can use the following rule to calculate the distance traveled for any number of minutes:

> Distance traveled = 8 ∗ number of minutes
>
> or
>
> $d = 8 * t$

where d stands for the distance traveled and t for the time of travel, in minutes. For example, after 1 minute, the plane will have traveled 8 miles (8 ∗ 1). After 2 minutes, it will have traveled 16 miles (8 ∗ 2).

1. Use the rule $d = 8 * t$ to complete the table at the right.

Time (min) (t)	Distance (mi) (8 ∗ t)
1	8
2	16
3	
4	
5	
6	
7	
8	
9	
10	

Use with Lesson 86.

Speed (continued)

2. Complete the graph using the data in the table on page 356. Then connect the dots.

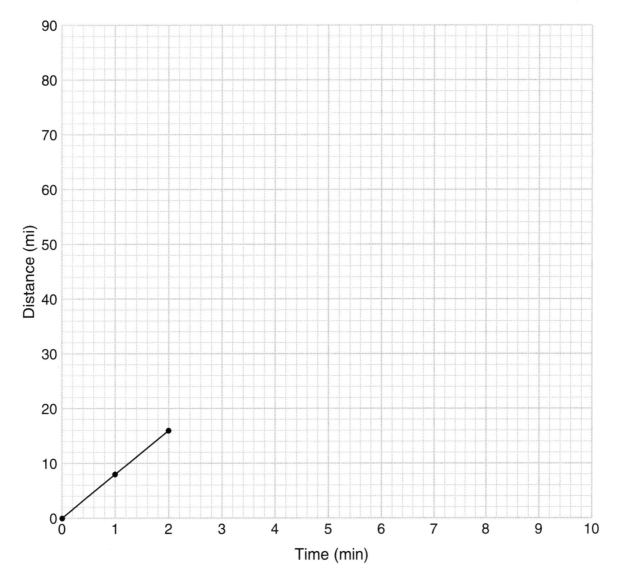

Use your graph to answer the following questions:

3. How far would the plane travel in $1\frac{1}{2}$ minutes?   _____ mi

4. How many miles would the plane travel in
   5 minutes 24 seconds (5.4 minutes)?   _____ mi

5. How long would it take the plane to travel 60 miles?   _____ min

Representing Rates

Complete each table below. Then graph the data and connect the points.

1. Andy earns $8 per hour. Rule: Earnings = $8 ∗ number of hours worked

Time (hr) (h)	Earnings ($) (8 ∗ h)
1	
2	
3	
	40
7	

Plot a point to show Andy's earnings for $5\frac{1}{2}$ hours. How much would he earn?

_____

2. Red peppers cost $2.50 a pound. Rule: Cost = $2.50 ∗ number of pounds

Weight (lb) (w)	Cost ($) ($2.50 ∗ w)
1	
2	
3	
	15
12	

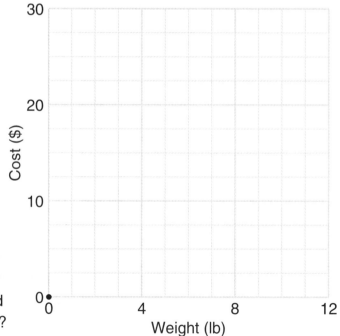

Plot a point to show the cost of 8 pounds. How much would 8 pounds of red peppers cost?

_____

Use with Lesson 86.

Representing Rates (continued)

3. Frank types an average of 45 words a minute.

Rule: Words typed = 45 ∗ number of minutes

Time (min) (*t*)	Words (45 ∗ *t*)
1	
2	
3	
	225
6	

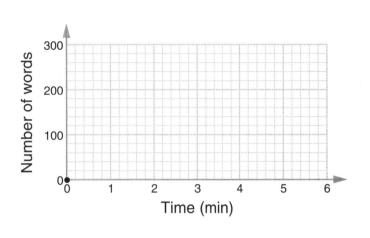

Plot a point to show the number of words Frank types in 4 minutes. How many words is that?

_____

4. Joan's car uses 1 gallon of gasoline every 28 miles.

Rule: Distance = 28 ∗ number of gallons

Gasoline (gal) (*g*)	Distance (mi) (28 ∗ *g*)
1	
2	
3	
	140
$5\frac{1}{2}$	

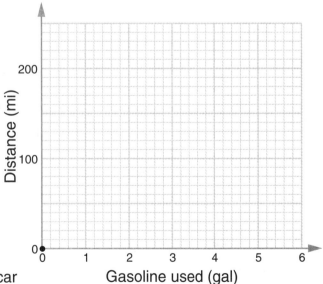

Plot a point to show how far the car would travel on 1.4 gallons of gasoline. How far would it travel?

_____

Use with Lesson 86.

Yellowstone—The World's Greatest Geyser Area

Old Faithful Geyser in Yellowstone National Park is one of nature's most impressive sights. Most of the time, Old Faithful is peaceful. Puffs of steam rise out of the ground and drift across mounds of gray stone.

Then the steam increases. Spurts of water rise 10, 20, 30 feet into the air and fall back. Finally, with a roar, a column of steam and superheated water climbs up, and up, and up—50, 100, 150 feet, and more. Water crashes to the ground while more steam and water rush skyward. The giant fountain may continue for nearly five minutes. Then it shortens and disappears … until next time.

Old Faithful is not the largest geyser in Yellowstone or the tallest. But it is the most dependable large geyser. Using the length of time of an eruption, park rangers can predict when the next eruption will begin.

Geysers are reminders that our planet Earth is very hot inside. In some places, such as Yellowstone, the hot interior is closer to the surface than in other places. Yellowstone has 200 geysers and thousands of hot springs, mud pots, steam vents, and other "hot spots"—more than any other place on Earth.

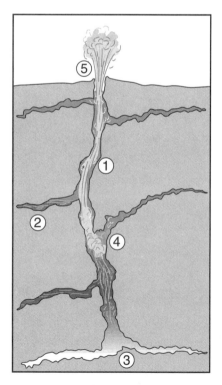

1 In a geyser, holes and tunnels in underground rock are connected to the surface by a narrow "neck."

2 Underground water fills the holes, tunnels, and neck. Earth heats the water.

3 The water at the bottom gets very hot—much hotter than the normal boiling temperature of water. It can't boil or get out because of the water above it. But it can expand by pushing water out at the top.

4 Then some of the water at the bottom explodes. It becomes steam.

5 The steam pushes the water above it up and out with great force, causing the geyser to **erupt.**

Predicting When Old Faithful Will Erupt Next

Old Faithful erupts at regular intervals that are **predictable.**

If you time the length of one eruption, you can **predict** about how long you must wait until the next eruption. Use this formula:

Waiting time = (10 * (length of eruption)) + 30 minutes

$$W = (10 * E) + 30$$

or $W = 10E + 30$

> All times are in minutes.

1. Use the formula to complete the table below.

Length of Eruption (min) (*E*)	Waiting Time to Next Eruption (min) ((10 * *E*) + 30)
2 min	50 min
3 min	min
4 min	min
5 min	min
1 min	min
$2\frac{1}{2}$ min	min
3 min 15 sec	min
min	45 min

2. Graph the data from the table. Two number pairs have been plotted for you.

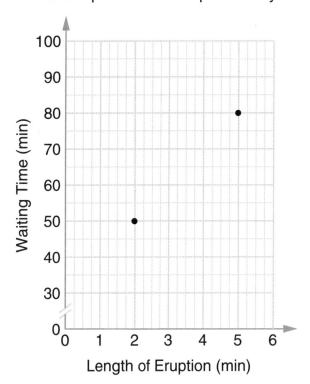

3. It's 8:30 A.M., and Old Faithful has just finished a 4-minute eruption. About when will it erupt next? _____

4. Old Faithful erupts for 3 minutes and 30 seconds. The eruption stops at 2:20 P.M. About when will it erupt next? _____

5. The average time between eruptions of Old Faithful is about 75 minutes. So the average length of an eruption is about how many minutes? _____

Math Boxes 87

1. Circle each problem whose answer is a prime number.

a. 88 ÷ 8

b. 43 * 2

c. 19 + 18

d. 51 + 32

e. 95 − 48

2. Insert parentheses to make each number sentence true.

a. 7 * 2 + 18 = 140

b. 98 = 18 / 9 * 49

c. 27 = 45 / 5 * 3

d. 6 * 7 − 6 = 6

e. 45 / 5 * 3 = 3

3. The smallest breed of dog is the Chihuahua. An average Chihuahua weighs about 3 pounds.

a. About how many ounces would 5 average Chihuahuas weigh?

_____ ounces

b. About how many ounces would 12 average Chihuahuas weigh?

_____ ounces

4. Solve.

a. $\frac{1}{3}$ of 27 = _____

b. $\frac{1}{8}$ of 40 = _____

c. $\frac{1}{5}$ of 100 = _____

d. $\frac{2}{5}$ of 100 = _____

e. $\frac{1}{4}$ of 60 = _____

5. Use your calculator to complete the table.

Exponential Notation	Product of Factors	Standard Notation
8^3		512
5^7	5 * 5 * 5 * 5 * 5 * 5 * 5	
	3 * 3 * 3 * 3 * 3	
6^4		
4^4		

Use with Lesson 87.

Math Boxes 88

---

1. Mark and label each point on the ruler below.

$A = \frac{8}{16}$ in $B = 1\frac{5}{8}$ in

$C = \frac{11}{16}$ in $D = 1\frac{9}{16}$ in

$E = 1\frac{15}{16}$ in

INCHES 0 1 2

2. I am a number. If you take $\frac{1}{3}$ of me and then double the result, you get 14.

What number am I? _____

---

3. **a.** Measure the base and height of the triangle below to the nearest centimeter.

The base is about _____ cm.

The height is about _____ cm.

b. Find the area of the triangle to the nearest square centimeter.

The area is about _____ cm².

Area = $\frac{1}{2} * b * h$

4. Write five names for 0.6.

_____

_____

_____

_____

_____

---

5. Solve.

a.   907
         − 249
         _____

b.   645
         − 493
         _____

c.   426
         − 384
         _____

d.   799
         + 266
         _____

e.   509
         + 321
         _____

f.   678
         + 453
         _____

Rules, Tables, and Graphs

1. Use the graph below. Find the *x*- and *y*-coordinates for each point shown.
   Then enter the *x* and *y* values in the table.

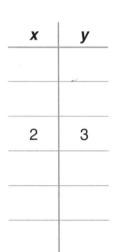

x	y
2	3

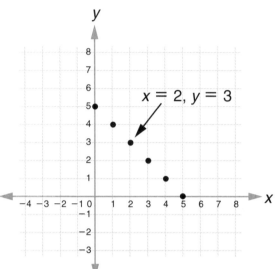

$x = 2, y = 3$

2. Eli is 10 years old and can run an average of 5 yards per second. His sister Sara is 7 and can run an average of 4 yards per second.

   Eli and Sara have a 60-yard race. Because Sara is younger, Eli gives her a 10-yard head start.

   Complete the table showing the distances Eli and Sara are from the starting line after 1 second, 2 seconds, 3 seconds, and so on.

   Use the table to answer the questions below.

   a. Who wins the race? _____

   b. What is the winning time?

   _____

   c. Who was in the lead during most of the race?

   _____

Time (sec)	Distance (yd)	
	Eli	Sara
start	0	10
1		
2		18
3	15	
4		
5		
6		
7		38
8		
9		
10		
11		
12		

Use with Lesson 88.

Rules, Tables, and Graphs (continued)

3. Use the grid below to graph the results of the race between Eli and Sara.

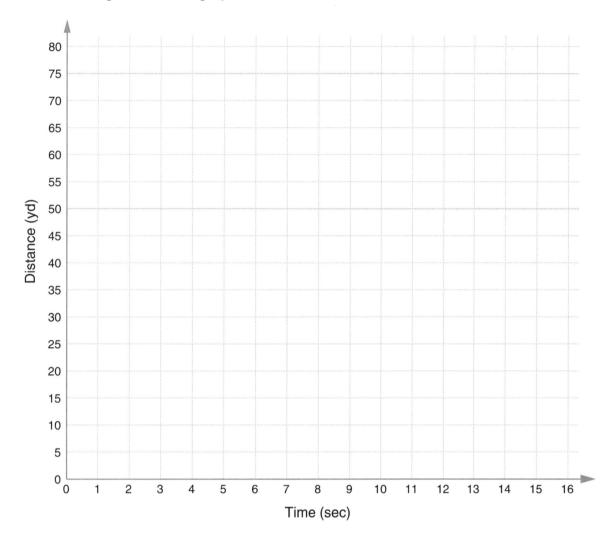

4. How many yards apart are Eli and Sara after 7 seconds? _____

5. Suppose that Eli and Sara race for 75 yards instead of 60 yards.

    a. Who would you expect to win? _____

    b. How long would the race last? _____ seconds

    c. How far ahead would the winner be at the finish line? _____ yards

Math Message: Adding and Subtracting Decimals

Use your calculator to solve these problems as quickly as you can.

1.
$$\begin{array}{r} 7.9 \\ + 8.8 \\ \hline \end{array}$$

2.
$$\begin{array}{r} 6.2 \\ - 2.9 \\ \hline \end{array}$$

3.
$$\begin{array}{r} 43.6 \\ - 21.9 \\ \hline \end{array}$$

4. $-5.63 - 2.24 =$ _____

5.
$$\begin{array}{r} 1.234 \\ + 2.789 \\ \hline \end{array}$$

6. $141 + 14.6 =$ _____

7.
$$\begin{array}{r} 1.2 \\ 3.4 \\ + 5.6 \\ \hline \end{array}$$

8. $5 + (-16.5) =$ _____

9.
$$\begin{array}{r} 5.0 \\ - 16.5 \\ \hline \end{array}$$

10. $5 - (-16.5) =$ _____

Use with Lesson 89.

Reading Graphs

1. Tom and Alisha run a 200-yard race. Tom has a head start.

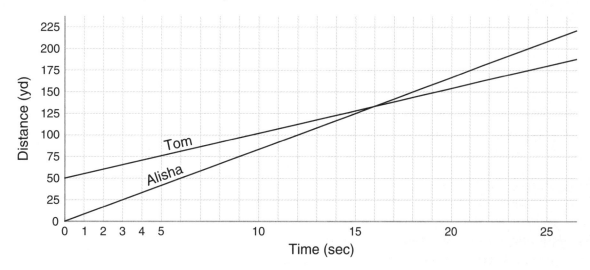

a. Who wins the race? _____

b. By about how much? _____

c. Mark the point on the graph where Alisha overtakes Tom.

d. About how many yards does Alisha run before taking the lead? _____

e. About how many seconds pass before Alisha takes the lead? _____

f. Who is ahead after 9 seconds? _____

g. By about how much? _____

2. Babar is definitely out of shape. But he runs 100 meters as fast as he can.

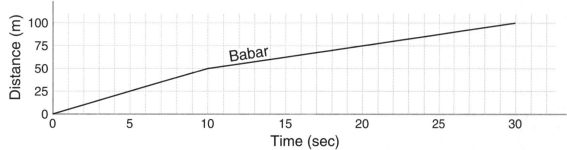

In the **first 10 seconds** of his run, Babar covers about _____ meters,

and his speed is about _____ meters per second.

In the **final 10 seconds** of his run, Babar covers about _____ meters,

and his speed is about _____ meters per second.

Mystery Graphs

Each of the events described below is represented by one of the following graphs:

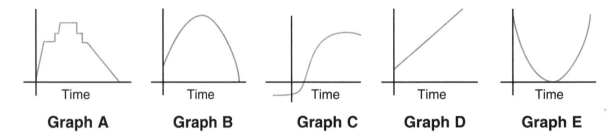

| Graph A | Graph B | Graph C | Graph D | Graph E |

Match each event with its graph.

1. A frozen dinner is removed from the
   freezer. It is heated in a microwave oven.
   Then it is placed on the table.

   Which graph shows the temperature
   of the dinner at different times?   _____

2. Satya runs water into his bathtub. He
   steps into the tub, sits down, and bathes.
   He gets out of the tub and drains the water.

   Which graph shows the height of water
   in the tub at different times?   _____

3. A baseball is thrown straight up into the air.

   a. Which graph shows the height of the
      ball—from the time it is thrown until
      the time it hits the ground?   _____

   b. Which graph shows the speed of the
      ball at different times?   _____

Math Boxes 89

1. Complete the pattern.

2, 3, 5, _____, 11, _____, 17, _____,

_____

2. Insert parentheses to make each number sentence true.

a. 6 + 8 * 10 = 140

b. 21 = 42 / 6 − 4

c. 7 * 7 + 2 = 63

d. 3 * 15 − 3 = 36

e. 42 / 6 − 4 = 3

3. A tuna swims at an average speed of about 9 miles per hour. Tuna don't sleep and don't stop moving.

a. About how many miles does a tuna travel in one day at an average speed of 9 miles per hour?

_____

b. What missing information did you need in order to answer Part a?

_____

Source: *Beyond Belief!!*

4. Solve.

a. $\frac{1}{3}$ of 36 = _____

b. $\frac{2}{5}$ of 75 = _____

c. $\frac{3}{8}$ of 88 = _____

d. $\frac{5}{6}$ of 30 = _____

e. $\frac{2}{7}$ of 28 = _____

5. Use your calculator to write the following in standard notation.

a. 5^4 = _____

b. 7^3 = _____

c. 6^5 = _____

d. 9^5 = _____

e. 4^4 = _____

The Swing Time of Pendulums

1. Your teacher will demonstrate the experiment with a 50-cm pendulum. Record the results below.

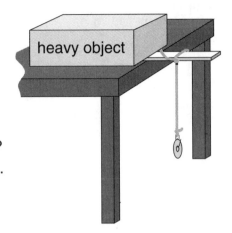

heavy object

   a. It took about _____ seconds for 10 complete swings of the pendulum.

   b. About how much time did it take for 1 swing? Write your answer to the nearest 0.1 second.

      _____ second(s)

2. Set your pendulum so that its length is 75 centimeters. Practice timing 10 complete swings of the pendulum. Time the swings to the nearest second. After you have practiced several times, time 10 swings one more time and record the results below.

   a. It took about _____ seconds for 10 complete swings of the pendulum.

   b. About how much time did it take for 1 swing? Write your answer to the nearest 0.1 second. _____ second(s)

3. Record the results for a 50-cm and a 75-cm pendulum in the table at the right.

4. Experiment with different lengths of pendulum string.

   Find the time for 10 complete swings for each of the other pendulum lengths. Time the 10 swings to the nearest 0.1 second. Record your results in the table.

   After collecting your data, divide each of the times by 10 to estimate the time for 1 complete swing. Record your answers in the table, to the nearest 0.1 second.

Length of pendulum	Time for:	
	10 complete swings (to nearest 0.1 sec)	1 complete swing (to nearest 0.1 sec)
5 cm	sec	sec
10 cm	sec	sec
20 cm	sec	sec
30 cm	sec	sec
50 cm	sec	sec
75 cm	sec	sec
100 cm	sec	sec
200 cm	sec	sec

Use with Lesson 90.

The Swing Time of Pendulums (continued)

Wait for instructions from your teacher before drawing the graph in Problem 5.

5. Construct a graph to show the amount of time it took for each length of the pendulum to complete 1 swing.

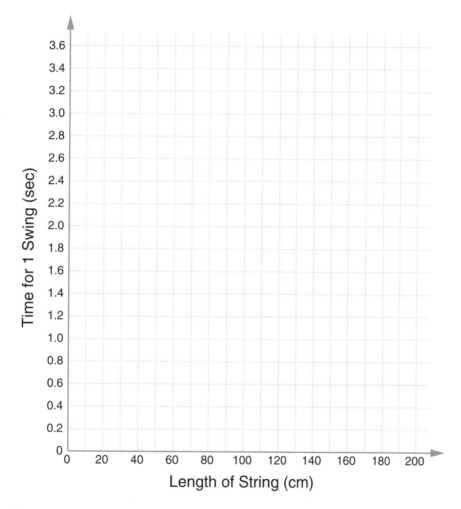

6. Experiment with different arc sizes. The largest arc is formed when the string of the pendulum is in a horizontal position. Does the size of the arc make much of a difference in the amount of time it takes for 10 complete swings?

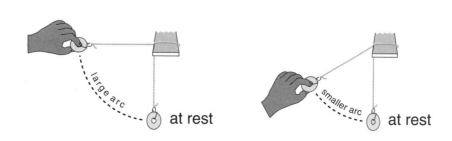

The Swing Time of Pendulums (continued)

7. Does the weight of the object attached to the end of a pendulum change the duration of a complete swing? Using the pendulum with the 50-cm length of string, try different numbers of objects to find out if weight makes a difference in the time of the swing.

Length of pendulum	Number of weights (washers or other objects)	Time for 10 swings (to nearest sec)	Time for 1 swing (to nearest 0.1 sec)
50 cm	1	sec	sec
50 cm	3	sec	sec
50 cm	5	sec	sec
50 cm	10	sec	sec

My conclusion: It seems that _____

_____

_____

_____

_____

_____

_____

A Long Time?

The Convention Center in Portland, Oregon, holds the longest pendulum in the world. The "string" is 90 feet long, and the "weight" is 900 pounds. Visitors may walk beneath the pendulum with the weight swinging 23 feet above their heads.

Source: *The Guinness Book of Records 1993.*

Use with Lesson 90.

Math Boxes 90

---

1. What is the distance from 0 to each point marked on the ruler?

A: _____ in

B: _____ in

C: _____ in

D: _____ in

E: _____ in

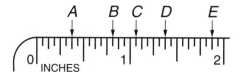

2. I am a number less than 50. If you take $\frac{1}{5}$ of me and divide the result by 3, you get 3.

What number am I? _____

---

3. Find the area and perimeter of the rectangle.

7 cm

$3\frac{1}{2}$ cm

Area = _____

Perimeter = _____

4. Write 5 names for 3.8.

_____

_____

_____

_____

_____

---

5. Add or subtract.

a. 478 + 3605 = _____

b. 249 + 627 = _____

c. 965 – 798 = _____

d. 1005 – 387 = _____

e. 243 – 195 = _____

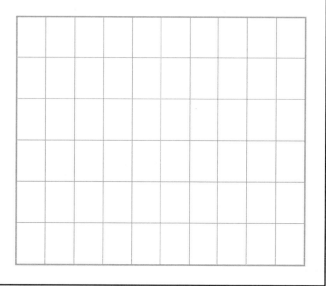

Time to Reflect

1. Suppose a new student moves to your school. The new student has never seen a pan-balance problem before. Make up such a problem and explain how to do it.

_____

_____

_____

_____

_____

_____

2. Look back through the work that you did in Units 5–8. Make a list of some of the strengths and weaknesses that you were able to find in your work.

_____

_____

_____

_____

_____

_____

3. Set a mathematical goal for yourself that you would like to accomplish. What will you do to help yourself achieve this goal?

_____

_____

_____

_____

_____

_____

Use with Lesson 91.

Math Boxes 91

1. a. One banana weighs as much

as _____ balls.

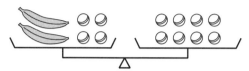

b. One orange weighs as much

as _____ blocks.

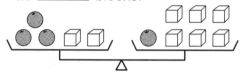

2. Use ⊞ and ⊟ counters to solve the following problems:

a. $-7 + (-3) =$ _____

b. $5 + (-8) =$ _____

c. $-17 + 10 =$ _____

d. $-15 + 15 =$ _____

e. $3 + (-20) =$ _____

3. Theresa is y years old. Write an algebraic expression for the age of each person below.

a. Nancy is four years older than Theresa. Nancy's age: _____

b. Frank is twice as old as Theresa. Frank's age: _____

c. José is $\frac{1}{3}$ as old as Theresa. José's age: _____

d. Lucienne is 8 years younger than Theresa. Lucienne's age: _____

e. If Theresa is 12, who is the oldest person above? _____

How old is that person? _____

4. Fran reads at a rate of 50 pages an hour. Complete the table; then graph the data in the table.

Rule
Total number of pages = 50 * number of hours

in	out
1	50
2	
	150
	250
7	

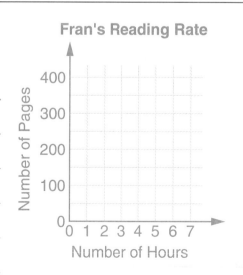

Fran's Reading Rate

Math Message: Comparing Fractions

Circle the greater fraction in each pair.

1. $\frac{3}{5}$ $\frac{4}{5}$

2. $\frac{4}{5}$ $\frac{4}{7}$

3. $\frac{5}{8}$ $\frac{5}{12}$

4. $\frac{6}{10}$ $\frac{7}{12}$

5. $\frac{3}{8}$ $\frac{4}{10}$

6. $\frac{3}{4}$ $\frac{7}{16}$

7. $\frac{7}{8}$ $\frac{6}{7}$

8. $\frac{5}{9}$ $\frac{3}{7}$

9. $\frac{15}{16}$ $\frac{11}{12}$

Be prepared to explain how you decided on each answer.

Reading a Ruler

1. On the ruler below, points *A* through *L* mark distances from the beginning of the ruler (0 inches). Give the distance from *0* for each point. Point *A* has been done for you.

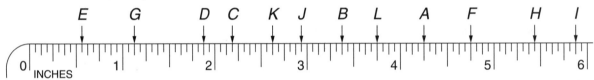

A: ____ $4\frac{1}{4}$ ____ in   B: _____ in   C: _____ in

D: _____ in   E: _____ in   F: _____ in

G: _____ in   H: _____ in   I: _____ in

J: _____ in   K: _____ in   L: _____ in

2. Pick four of the points above. For each point, write an equivalent name for its distance from 0.

   Example: ___ *A* : ____ $4\frac{1}{4}$ ____ in = ____ $4\frac{4}{16}$ ____ in

   ___ : _____ in = _____ in

   ___ : _____ in = _____ in

   ___ : _____ in = _____ in

   ___ : _____ in = _____ in

Use with Lesson 92.

Fractions

You've heard and used fraction words even before you started school (for example, "I want half of that cookie!"), and, since then, you have used fraction notation and fraction ideas in many ways. Here is a brief summary of fraction uses, for reminder and reference as you complete *Fifth Grade Everyday Mathematics.*

Notation	$\frac{a}{b}$ or *a/b,* where the **numerator** *a* can be any number at all and the **denominator** *b* is any number except zero. $\frac{a}{b}$ ← numerator ← denominator $b \neq 0$
Many Names	Any number can be written as a fraction in thousands of ways, by multiplying or dividing both numerator and denominator by the same number (except 0). That same number also has decimal and percent names, which can be found from any of its fraction names by dividing the numerator by the denominator.

$\frac{1}{2}=\frac{2}{4}=\frac{3}{6}=\frac{4}{8}=\frac{5}{10}=\frac{6}{12}=\frac{7}{14}=\frac{8}{16}=\frac{9}{18}=\frac{10}{20}=\frac{11}{22}=\frac{12}{24}=\frac{13}{26}=\frac{14}{28}=\frac{15}{30}$	0.5	50%
$\frac{1}{3}=\frac{2}{6}=\frac{3}{9}=\frac{4}{12}=\frac{5}{15}=\frac{6}{18}=\frac{7}{21}=\frac{8}{24}=\frac{9}{27}=\frac{10}{30}=\frac{11}{33}=\frac{12}{36}=\frac{13}{39}=\frac{14}{42}=\frac{15}{45}$	$0.\overline{3}$	$33\frac{1}{3}\%$

Using Equal Names	Two fractions can be compared by using names with the same denominator. One way to add or subtract fractions is by finding names with the same denominator. You can also use the decimal names to decide which is bigger or smaller or to add and subtract. $\frac{2}{3} < \frac{3}{4}$ since $\frac{8}{12} < \frac{9}{12}$ and $0.\overline{6} < 0.75$ $\frac{3}{4} - \frac{3}{5} = \frac{15}{20} - \frac{12}{20} = \frac{3}{20}$ or $\frac{3}{4} - \frac{3}{5} = 0.75 - 0.60 = 0.15$

Uses	**Parts of Wholes** Fractions are used to name a part of a whole object or a part of a collection of objects. $\frac{5}{6}$ of the hexagon is shaded. $\frac{6}{10}$ of the dimes are circled. **Points on Number Lines** Fractions can name points on a number line that are "in-between" the points named with whole numbers.

Fractions (continued)

Uses	

"In-Between" Measures
Fractions can name measures that are "in-between" whole measures.

Division Notation
The fraction a/b is another way of saying a divided by b.

$$a \div b \qquad b\,)\overline{\,a\,}$$

Ratios
Fractions are used to compare quantities with the same unit.

Curie won 7 out of 17 games ($\frac{7}{17}$ or about 41%) during last year's basketball season.

PUBLIC-RED CENTRAL		
	Conf.	Overall
Dunbar	4–0	9–6
King	4–1	14–4
Robeson	3–2	8–9
Gage Park	2–3	8–10
Harper	2–4	8–7
Curie	1–3	7–10
Hubbard	1–4	8–9

Rates
Fractions are used to compare quantities with different units.

Bill's car can travel about 35 miles on 1 gallon of gasoline. At this rate, it can travel about 245 miles on 7 gallons of gasoline. $\frac{35}{1} = \frac{245}{7}$

Scales
Fractions are used to compare the size of a drawing or model to the size of the actual object.

For example, a scale on a map given as 1:100,000 (another way of expressing 1/100,000) means that each inch on the map represents 100,000 inches, or about $1\frac{1}{2}$ miles.

Probabilities
Fractions are a way to describe the chance that an event will happen.

In a well-shuffled playing card deck (52 cards), the chance of selecting the ace of spades on a given draw is $\frac{1}{52}$, or about 2%. The chance of drawing any ace is $\frac{4}{52}$ or about 8%.

Miscellaneous
People use fractions in a variety of ways every day.

The critic gave the new movie $3\frac{1}{2}$ stars.

The stock closed at $14\frac{5}{8}$—down $1\frac{1}{2}$ dollars from yesterday.

It was a half-baked idea—I'm not surprised that it didn't work.

378

Use with Lesson 92.

Build-It

Materials   ☐ calculator
☐ one deck of 16 *Build-It* fraction cards (Activity Sheet 17)
☐ one *Build-It* gameboard per player (*Journal 2*, p. 380)

Number of players 2

Object of the game To be the first player to arrange five fraction cards from smallest to largest.

Directions

1. Shuffle the fraction cards. Deal one card facedown on each of the 5 spaces on each player's *Build-It* gameboard.

2. Put the remaining cards facedown in a pile. Turn the top card over and place it in a discard pile.

3. Each player turns over the 5 cards on his or her *Build-It* gameboard. Players must not change the order of the cards at any time during the game.

4. Players take turns, as follows:

   a. The player takes either the top card from the face-down pile or the top card from the discard pile.

   b. The player decides whether to keep this card or put it faceup on top of the discard pile.

   c. If the player keeps the card, it must replace one of the player's 5 cards on the *Build-It* gameboard. The player puts the replaced card faceup on the discard pile.

5. If all the face-down cards are used, shuffle the discard pile, repeat Step 2, and continue playing.

6. The winner is the first player to have all 5 cards on his or her gameboard in order from the smallest fraction to the largest.

Build-It Gameboard

Closest
to 1

Closest
to 0

Use with Lesson 92.

Algebra Election

Materials
- ❏ 4 pennies or other small counters
- ❏ 1 six-sided die
- ❏ Electoral Vote Map (Masters 65 and 66)
- ❏ 32 *Algebra Election* Problem Cards (Activity Sheets 18 and 19)
- ❏ pencil, scratch paper, and calculator

Number of players Two teams, each with 2 players

Object of the game Players move their counters around on a map of the United States. For each state a player lands on, the player tries to win that state's electoral votes by solving a problem. Players may also land on the District of Columbia (DC) and try to win its votes. The first team to collect 270 or more votes wins the election. Winning team members become president and vice president.

Directions

1. Each player puts a counter on Iowa (IA).

2. One member of each team rolls the die. The team with the higher roll goes first. Turns alternate between teams and partners:

   Team 1, Player 1; Team 2, Player 1; Team 1, Player 2; Team 2, Player 2.

3. Shuffle the *Algebra Election* Problem Cards and place them facedown in a pile.

4. The first player rolls the die. The result tells how many moves the player must make from the current state. Each new state counts as one move. Moves can be in any direction as long as they pass between states that share a common border. *Exceptions:* Players can get to and from Alaska by way of Washington and to and from Hawaii by way of California. Once a player has been in a state, the player cannot return to that state on the same turn.

5. The player makes the indicated number of moves and puts the counter in the last state landed on.

6. The player takes the top Problem Card. The state's number of electoral votes is substituted for x in the problem(s) on the card. The player solves the problem(s) and offers an answer. The other team checks the answer. Both the player solving the problem and the team checking the answer may use calculators for all problems.

Algebra Election (continued)

7. If the answer is correct, the player's team wins the state's electoral votes. Team members do the following:

- Write the state's name and the corresponding number of electoral votes on scratch paper.

- Write their first initials in pencil on the state to show that they have won it.

Once a team wins a state, that state is out of play. The opposing team members may land on the state, but they can not win its votes.

8. If the partners do not solve the problem(s) correctly, the state remains open. Any player may land on it and try to win its votes in a later turn.

9. The next player rolls the die and moves her or his counter.

10. The first team to get at least 270 votes wins the election.

Notes

- In the rules, "state" means "state or District of Columbia (DC)."

- Partners may explain the problem(s) to each other. Each player, however, has to answer the problem(s) on her or his own.

- If a player does not want to answer a problem or problems, the player can say "Pass" and draw another card. A player may declare "Pass" twice during each round (32 cards).

- Some Problem Cards have several problems. In order to win a state's votes, the player must answer all questions correctly.

- It's helpful to have a strategy. Partners should look at the map to see which states have the most votes and then work together to win those states.

- When all the Problem Cards have been used, shuffle and use them again.

- Each player begins a turn from the last state he or she landed on.

- Some people who have played the game before suggest the following:

  Agree on a time limit for answering problems.

  Give 1 extra point if the player can name the capital of the state landed on.

- A shorter version of the game can be played by going through all 32 cards just once. The team with the most votes is then declared the winner.

382

Math Boxes 92

---

1. Draw a figure that has an area of 15 square units and a perimeter of 19 units.

1 unit   1 square unit

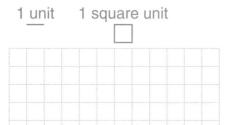

2. Multiply.

a. 70 * 2000 = _____

b. 300 * 500 = _____

c. 5000 × 600 = _____

d. _____ = 90 * 400

e. _____ = 80 × 4000

---

3. During the 1960 Winter Olympics, the winning time for the 500-meter women's speed-skating race was 45.9 seconds. In 1972, the winning time was 43.33 seconds. How much faster was the 1972 time than the 1960 time?

_____

4. Death Valley, California has an elevation of two hundred eighty-two feet below sea level.

a. How would you write this elevation with digits?

_____

b. From Death Valley, how many feet would you have to climb to reach sea level?

_____

c. What number can you use to represent sea level?

_____

---

5. Draw a line segment that is $2\frac{1}{4}$ inches long. Mark and label the following points on the line segment the given distance from the left endpoint.

$A = \frac{11}{16}$ in $B = \frac{1}{8}$ in

$C = 1\frac{3}{16}$ in $D = 1\frac{7}{8}$ in

6. Write an algebraic expression for each of the following.

Karl has *M* marbles in his collection.

a. Kristine has 3 times as many marbles as Karl.

_____

b. Lenny has 8 more than $\frac{1}{2}$ as many marbles as Karl.

_____

Math Message: Using a Ruler

1. Mark each of these lengths on the ruler shown below. Write the letter above your mark. Point *A* has been done for you.

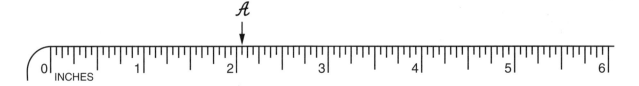

A: $2\frac{1}{16}$ in   B: $4\frac{3}{8}$ in   C: $3\frac{3}{4}$ in   D: $1\frac{7}{16}$ in   E: $2\frac{4}{8}$ in

2. Measure the following line segments to the nearest $\frac{1}{16}$ of an inch.

   a. ———————————————————

   _____ in

   b. ———

   _____ in

   c. ———————————————————————

   _____ in

   d. ————————————————

   _____ in

3. Draw a line segment that is $4\frac{3}{16}$ inches long.

4. Draw a line segment that is $3\frac{1}{2}$ inches long.

5. Complete these ruler puzzles.

   Example: $\frac{1}{4}$ in $= \frac{x}{8}$ in $= \frac{y}{16}$ in $x =$ ___2___ $y =$ ___4___

   a. $\frac{6}{8}$ in $= \frac{x}{16}$ in $= \frac{3}{y}$ in $x =$ _____ $y =$ _____

   b. $3\frac{2}{8}$ in $= 3\frac{m}{4}$ in $= 3\frac{4}{n}$ in $m =$ _____ $n =$ _____

   c. $\frac{6}{r}$ in $= \frac{12}{s}$ in $= \frac{t}{4}$ in $r =$ _____ $s =$ _____ $t =$ _____

Addition and Subtraction of Fractions on a Slide Rule

1. Use your slide rule, or any other method, to add or subtract.

   a. $\frac{1}{2} + \frac{1}{4} =$ _____

   b. $\frac{5}{8} + \frac{2}{8} =$ _____

   c. $2\frac{1}{2} + 3 =$ _____

   d. $3\frac{5}{8} + 3\frac{3}{4} =$ _____

   e. $1\frac{9}{16} + 1\frac{5}{16} =$ _____

   f. $7/8 - 3/8 =$ _____

   g. $5\frac{3}{4} - 2\frac{1}{4} =$ _____

   h. $7\frac{1}{2} - 4\frac{5}{8} =$ _____

   i. $\frac{19}{16} - \frac{1}{2} =$ _____

   j. $5\frac{1}{2} - 6 =$ _____

2. Put a star next to the problems above that you thought were the easiest.

3. Complete the following: It is easy to add or subtract fractions with the same denominator (for example, $\frac{3}{8} + \frac{4}{8}$) because …

   _____

   _____

   _____

   _____

   _____

Did You Know

Prime Time

When this book went to the printer, the largest known prime number was equal to $2^{2,976,221} - 1$, a number with 895,932 digits. If these digits were printed on one line, 6 digits to a centimeter, they would stretch almost 1.5 kilometers. Checking that this number is prime took 15 days on a desktop computer. By the time you read this, larger prime numbers will probably have been found.

Large prime numbers have practical applications in science and engineering. One use is in testing for defects in computer chips. More about the search for prime numbers can be found on the Internet at http://www.mersenne.org/.

Source: *Science News.*

Fraction Sticks

1. Write the missing fraction for each pair of fraction sticks.
   Then write the sum or difference of the fractions.

   a. $\frac{5}{12}$ + _____ = _____

   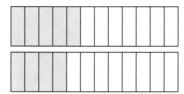

   b. $\frac{5}{6}$ − _____ = _____

   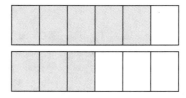

   c. _____ − $\frac{1}{4}$ = _____

   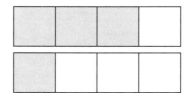

2. Andy jogs on a track where each lap is $\frac{1}{4}$ mile. Find the number
   of miles he jogged each day and then the total number of laps
   and miles for the three days.

Day	Laps	Distance
Monday	5	mi
Wednesday	10	mi
Thursday	8	mi
Total		mi

Use with Lesson 93.

Math Boxes 93

---

1. Circle the display that shows all the following data landmarks.

Maximum: 22   Range: 18   Mode: 16   Median: 12

Stems (10s)	Leaves (1s)
0	4 7 8 9 9
1	0 1 2 6 6 6 6
2	1 2

4	3
10	6
11	3
12	3
16	8
20	2
22	1

```
                                    x
            x     x        x        x
        x   x  x  x  x     x        x   x
      ─────────────────────────────────────
        4   6  8  10 12 14 16 18 20 22
```

---

2. Multiply or divide.

   a.   749
         × 247

   b.   384
         * 856

   c.   923/72 → _____

   d.   1655/19 → _____

   e.   2240 ÷ 24 → _____

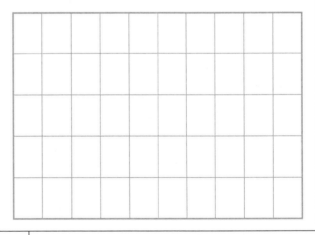

---

3. Write five names for $1\frac{4}{8}$.

_____

_____

_____

_____

_____

---

4. Insert parentheses to make the number sentences true.

   a.   3 * 8 − 2 = 18

   b.   60 = 3 + 3 * 10

   c.   24 / 8 * 9 = 27

   d.   32 = 12 − 4 * 4

   e.   30 / 5 + 1 = 7

Use with Lesson 93.

Math Message: Clock Fractions

The numbers on a clock face divide one hour into twelfths. Each $\frac{1}{12}$ of an hour is 5 minutes.

Whole
hour

1. How many minutes does each fraction represent? The first one has been done for you.

    a. $\frac{1}{12}$ hr = ___5___ min   b. $\frac{5}{12}$ hr = _____ min   c. $\frac{1}{2}$ hr = _____ min

    d. $\frac{1}{3}$ hr = _____ min   e. $\frac{1}{4}$ hr = _____ min   f. $\frac{1}{6}$ hr = _____ min

2. Using the clock face, fill in the missing numbers. The first one has been done for you.

    a. $\frac{1}{4}$ hr = $\frac{3}{12}$ hr   b. $\frac{8}{12}$ hr = $\frac{\square}{3}$ hr   c. $\frac{1}{3}$ hr = $\frac{2}{\square}$ hr

    d. $\frac{\square}{12}$ hr = $\frac{5}{6}$ hr   e. $\frac{3}{\square}$ hr = $\frac{9}{12}$ hr   f. $\frac{2}{12}$ hr = $\frac{\square}{6}$ hr

    g. $1\frac{1}{2}$ hr = $\frac{\square}{4}$ hr   h. $\frac{5}{3}$ hr = $\frac{\square}{12}$ hr   i. $\frac{4}{12}$ hr = $\frac{1}{\square}$ hr

3. Use clock fractions, if helpful, to solve these problems. Write each answer as a fraction.

    Example: $\frac{3}{4} - \frac{1}{3} = ?$

    Think: 45 minutes − 20 minutes = 25 minutes

    So $\frac{3}{4} - \frac{1}{3} = \frac{5}{12}$

    a. $\frac{5}{12} + \frac{3}{12}$ = _____   b. 3/6 + 1/6 = _____

    c. $\frac{3}{4} + \frac{2}{4}$ = _____   d. $\frac{11}{12} - \frac{3}{12}$ = _____

    e. $1 - \frac{2}{3}$ = _____   f. $\frac{5}{4} - \frac{2}{4}$ = _____

    g. $\frac{2}{3} + \frac{1}{6}$ = _____   h. $\frac{1}{4} + \frac{1}{3}$ = _____

    i. $\frac{1}{3} - \frac{1}{4}$ = _____   j. $\frac{5}{6} - \frac{3}{4}$ = _____

388

Using a Common Denominator

Study the examples. Then work the problems below in the same way.

Example: $\frac{2}{3} + \frac{1}{6} = ?$

Different Denominators		Common Denominators
$\frac{2}{3}$	$\frac{2}{3} = \frac{4}{6}$	$\frac{4}{6}$
$+ \frac{1}{6}$		$+ \frac{1}{6}$
		$\frac{5}{6}$

Example: $\frac{5}{6} - \frac{3}{4} = ?$

Different Denominators		Common Denominators
$\frac{5}{6}$	$\frac{5}{6} = \frac{10}{12}$	$\frac{10}{12}$
$- \frac{3}{4}$	$\frac{3}{4} = \frac{9}{12}$	$- \frac{9}{12}$
		$\frac{1}{12}$

---

1. $\frac{2}{3} + \frac{2}{9} = ?$

Different Denominators	Common Denominators
$\frac{2}{3}$	
$+ \frac{2}{9}$	

2. $\frac{13}{16} - \frac{3}{4} = ?$

Different Denominators	Common Denominators
$\frac{13}{16}$	
$- \frac{3}{4}$	

3. $\frac{1}{3} + \frac{2}{5} = ?$

Different Denominators	Common Denominators
$\frac{1}{3}$	
$+ \frac{2}{5}$	

4. $\frac{5}{6} - \frac{4}{9} = ?$

Different Denominators	Common Denominators
$\frac{5}{6}$	
$- \frac{4}{9}$	

Using a Common Denominator (continued)

5. $\frac{12}{4} + \frac{3}{2} = ?$

   Different   Common
   Denominators   Denominators

$$\frac{12}{4}$$

$$+\frac{3}{2}$$
_____   _____

6. $1\frac{1}{16} - \frac{3}{8} = ?$

   Different   Common
   Denominators   Denominators

$$1\frac{1}{16}$$

$$-\frac{3}{8}$$
_____   _____

7. A piece of ribbon is $7\frac{1}{2}$ inches long. If a piece $2\frac{3}{16}$ inches long is cut off, how long is the remaining piece? _____ in

8. Three boards are glued together. The diagram below shows the thickness of each board. What is the total thickness of the three boards? _____ in

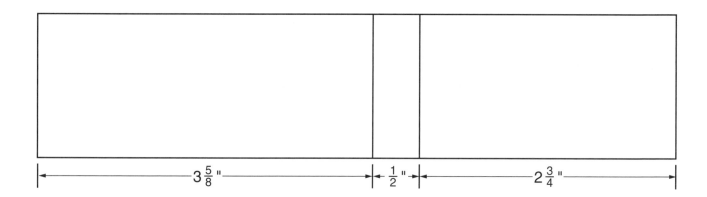

$\longleftarrow 3\frac{5}{8}" \longrightarrow$ $\leftarrow\frac{1}{2}"\rightarrow$ $\longleftarrow 2\frac{3}{4}" \longrightarrow$

Use with Lesson 94.

Math Boxes 94

1. **a.** Draw a circle with a radius of 1.5 centimeters.

b. Find the area of the circle.

The area is about _____ cm².

$$\boxed{Area = \pi * r^2}$$

2. Solve.

Solution:

a. $8 * d = 80$ _____

b. $45/e = 9$ _____

c. $s - 79 = 180$ _____

d. $t/9 = 7$ _____

e. $217 + m = 300$ _____

3. Name a number between each pair of numbers.

a. -1.30 and -1.20 _____

b. 8.05 and 8.10 _____

c. -0.26 and -0.25 _____

d. $\frac{1}{3}$ and $\frac{7}{8}$ _____

e. $\frac{1}{4}$ and 0.3 _____

f. 0.2 and $\frac{2}{9}$ _____

4. Complete the table and graph the data. Connect the points with line segments.

Marissa runs at an average speed of 6 miles per hour.

Rule
Miles run = 6 mi/hr * hours run

hours	miles
1	
2	
	30
6	
	48

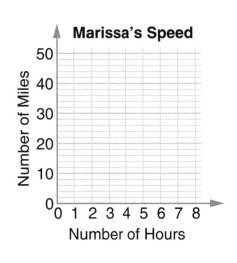

Marissa's Speed

Number of Miles

Number of Hours

Another Way to Find a Common Denominator

1. a. If each part of a fraction stick that shows $\frac{1}{3}$ is split into 5 equal parts, how any parts will there be in all? _____

   b. If each part of a fraction stick that shows $\frac{1}{5}$ is split into 3 equal parts, how many parts will there be in all? _____

   c. $\dfrac{1 * \boxed{}}{3 * \boxed{}} = \dfrac{5}{15}$ $\qquad$ $\dfrac{1 * \boxed{}}{5 * \boxed{}} = \dfrac{3}{15}$

2. a. If each part of a fraction stick that shows $\frac{3}{4}$ is split into 6 equal parts, how many parts will there be in all? _____

   b. If each part of a fraction stick that shows $\frac{5}{6}$ is split into 4 equal parts, how many parts will there be in all? _____

   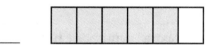

   c. $\dfrac{3 * \boxed{}}{4 * \boxed{}} = \dfrac{18}{24}$ $\qquad$ $\dfrac{5 * \boxed{}}{6 * \boxed{}} = \dfrac{20}{24}$

3. One way to find a common denominator for a pair of fractions is to make a list of equivalent fractions.

   $$\frac{3}{4} = \frac{6}{8} = \frac{9}{12} = \frac{12}{16} = \frac{15}{20} = \frac{18}{24}$$

   $$\frac{5}{6} = \frac{10}{12} = \frac{15}{18} = \frac{20}{24}$$

   Another way to find a common denominator for a pair of fractions is…

   _____

4. Give the value of the variables to make each equation true.

   a. $\dfrac{4 * t}{7 * t} = \dfrac{12}{21}$ $\qquad$ b. $\dfrac{4 * m}{6 * m} = \dfrac{n}{30}$ $\qquad$ c. $\dfrac{8 * x}{5 * x} = \dfrac{y}{45}$

   $t =$ _____ $\qquad$ $m =$ _____ $n =$ _____ $\qquad$ $x =$ _____ $y =$ _____

5. Name a common denominator for each pair of fractions.

   a. $\frac{3}{4}$ and $\frac{5}{16}$ _____ $\qquad$ b. $\frac{5}{8}$ and $\frac{9}{10}$ _____ $\qquad$ c. $\frac{4}{5}$ and $\frac{5}{6}$ _____

Use with Lesson 95.

Finding a Common Denominator

Common denominators are useful not only for adding and subtracting fractions, but also for comparing fractions.

A quick way to find a common denominator for a pair of fractions is to find the product of the denominators.

Example: Compare $\frac{2}{3}$ and $\frac{5}{8}$.

$$\frac{2}{3} = \frac{2*8}{3*8} = \frac{16}{24}$$

$$\frac{5}{8} = \frac{5*3}{8*3} = \frac{15}{24}$$

So $\frac{2}{3} > \frac{5}{8}$.

1. Rewrite each pair of fractions below using the same (common) denominator. Then use a greater than (>) or less than (<) symbol to show which fraction is larger.

	original fraction	equivalent fraction	> or <
a.	$\frac{4}{7}$ $\frac{3}{5}$		$\frac{4}{7}$ ☐ $\frac{3}{5}$
b.	$\frac{9}{4}$ $\frac{7}{3}$		$\frac{9}{4}$ ☐ $\frac{7}{3}$

2. Find a common denominator. Then add or subtract.

a. $\frac{1}{2} - \frac{1}{3} =$ _____

b. $\frac{7}{8} + \frac{2}{5} =$ _____

c. $3/4 - 1/2 =$ _____

d. $4/5 + 2/3 =$ _____

e. $\frac{9}{10}$
$- \frac{5}{6}$
———

f. $\frac{1}{10}$
$+ \frac{3}{4}$
———

Math Boxes 95

---

1. Find the perimeter and area of the rectangle below.

6 units

4 units

Perimeter: _____

Area: _____

2. Multiply.

a. 900 * 300 = _____

b. 1500 * 40 = _____

c. _____ = 7000 × 400

d. _____ = 6000 × 700

e. _____ = 800 * 800

---

3. Joan bought a dress for $45.81, a pair of shoes for $30.95, and a purse for $12.85. How much more did she spend on the dress than she spent on the shoes?

_____

4. During January, Barrow, Alaska, has an average temperature of $-13°F$. During the same month, Fairbanks, Alaska, has an average temperature of $-10°F$.

a. Which city has a warmer average temperature for January?

_____

b. How many degrees below freezing is $-13°F$?

_____

---

5. Draw a line segment that is $1\frac{3}{4}$ inches long. Mark and label the following points on the line segment the given distance from the left endpoint.

$A = \frac{5}{16}$ in $B = \frac{5}{8}$ in

$C = 1\frac{12}{16}$ in $D = 1\frac{1}{8}$ in

6. Write an algebraic expression for each of the following.

Michael earns D dollars an hour.

a. Melissa earns $7 more an hour than Michael.

_____

b. Nora earns twice as much an hour as Michael.

_____

c. Pedro earns $\frac{1}{3}$ as much an hour as Michael.

_____

Use with Lesson 95.

Calculator Key Investigation

Explore the six function keys on your calculator. Record what each function key does and give an example of its use.

Key	Function of Key	Example
[UNIT]		
[/]		
[F⟳D]		
[SIMP]		
[Ab/c]		
[x⟳y]		

Fraction Action, Fraction Friction

Materials   ❏ 1 *Fraction Action, Fraction Friction* card deck from
                    Activity Sheet 20
                  ❏ calculator

Number of players 2 or 3

Object To gather a set of fraction cards with a sum as close as possible to 2, without going over.

Directions Shuffle the *Fraction Action, Fraction Friction* cards. Deal one card to each player. The player with the fraction closest to $\frac{1}{2}$ begins the game.

Players return their cards to the deck. Shuffle the deck again. Place the pile facedown between the players.

Players take turns. At each turn:

1. The player takes a card from the top of the pile and places it faceup in front of him or her.

2. At each turn, the player must announce one of the following:

    ACTION!

    The player wants an additional card. The player believes that the sum of his or her cards is not close enough to 2 to win the hand. The player thinks that if he or she asks for another card, there is a good chance that the sum of the cards will be even closer to 2 than it is now, without going over.

    FRICTION!

    The player does not want an additional card. The player believes that the sum of his or her cards is close enough to 2 to possibly win the hand. The player thinks that if he or she asks for another card, there is a good chance that the sum of the cards will be greater than 2.

Play continues until all players have announced "Friction!" or have a set of cards whose sum is greater than 2. The player whose cards have the sum closest to 2 without going over is the winner of the hand. Players may check each other's sums on their calculators.

Reshuffle the cards and begin again. The winner of the game is the first person to win 5 hands.

Math Boxes 96

---

1. a. Make up a set of 12 numbers with the following landmarks.

     Minimum: 10
     Range: 8
     Median: 12
     Mode: 11

     _____

     _____

     _____

b. Make a bar graph for the data.

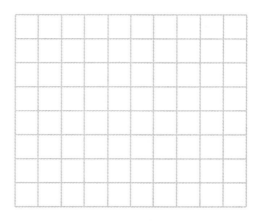

---

2. Multiply or divide.

     a. $654 * 229 =$ _____

     b. $382 * 701 =$ _____

     c. _____ $= 493 \times 287$

     d. $563 \div 18 \rightarrow$ _____

     e. $2078 \div 43 \rightarrow$ _____

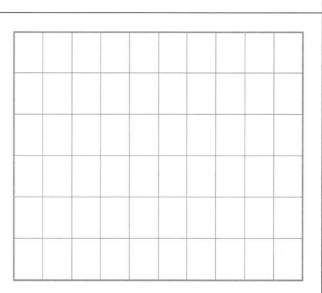

---

3. Write five other names for $\frac{36}{6}$.

     _____

     _____

     _____

     _____

     _____

4. Circle the expression in each pair with the greater value.

     a. $5 * (7 - 8)$ or $(5 * 7) - 8$

     b. $(30/2) + 5$ or $30/(2 + 5)$

     c. $(3 * 6) + (4 * 4)$ or

            $3 * (6 + 4) * 4$

     d. $9 + (9/3)$ or $(9 + 9)/3$

     e. $(18 - 12)/6$ or $18 - 12/6$

Math Message

1. Write all the pairs of factors whose product is 48. One pair has been done for you.

   $48 = 6 * 8;$ _____

2. One way to write 36 as a product of factors is $2 * 18$. Another way is $2 * 2 * 9$. Write 36 as the product of the longest possible string of factors. Do not include 1 as a factor.

   _____

Factor Trees

One way to find all the prime factors of a number is to make a **factor tree.** First, write the number. Then, underneath, write any two factors whose product is that number. Then write factors of each of these factors. Continue until all the factors are prime numbers. Below are three factor trees for 36.

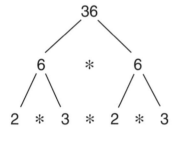 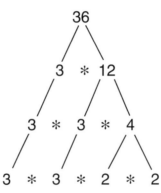 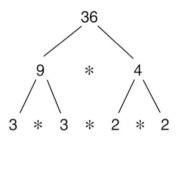

It does not matter which two factors you begin with. You always end with the same prime factors; for 36, they are 2, 2, 3, and 3. The **prime factorization** of 36 is $2 * 2 * 3 * 3$.

3. Make a factor tree for each number. Then write the prime factorization.

   a.   24   b.   50

   24 = _____   50 = _____

Factor Trees and Greatest Common Factors

1. Make a factor tree for each number below.

   a.   15   b.   75   c.   90

2. a. What prime factors do 15 and 75 have in common?   _____

   b. What is the greatest common factor for 15 and 75?   _____

   c. What is the greatest common factor for 75 and 90?   _____

   d. What is the greatest common factor for 15, 75, and 90?   _____

3. Use the factor trees in Problem 1 to help you write each fraction below in simplest form. Divide the numerator and denominator by their **greatest common factor.**

   a. $\frac{15}{75} =$ b. $\frac{15}{90} =$ c. $\frac{75}{90} =$

4. What is the greatest common factor for 20 and 25?
   (You may use factor trees to help you.)   _____

Multiples and Denominators

The **least common multiple** for two numbers is the smallest number that is a multiple of both numbers.

Example:

Multiples of 6 are 6, 12, 18, **24,** 30, 36, 42, **48,** 54, and so on.

Multiples of 8 are 8, 16, **24,** 32, 40, **48,** 56, and so on.

24 and 48 are in both lists. They are common multiples.

24 is the smallest. It is the **least common multiple** for 6 and 8.

It is also the smallest number that can be divided evenly by both numbers.

Another way to find the **least common multiple** for two numbers is to use prime factorizations.

The prime factorizations for 8 and 12 are shown below. You may make factor trees to show these factorizations.

$$8 = 2 * 2 * 2$$

$$12 = 2 * 2 * 3$$

To find the least common multiple, first circle pairs of common factors. Then cross out one factor in each pair, as shown below.

$$8 = 2 * 2 * 2$$
$$12 = 2 * 2 * 3$$

The factors that are not crossed out are factors of the **least common multiple.** The least common multiple of 8 and 12 is $2 * 2 * 2 * 3$, or 24.

Twenty-four is also the least common denominator for the fractions $\frac{1}{8}$ and $\frac{1}{12}$ (or any other fractions with denominators 8 and 12). In general, for two fractions *a/b* and *c/d,* the least common multiple is a common denominator, and in fact, the least common denominator.

Multiples and Denominators (continued)

1. Make factor trees and write the prime factorizations for the following.

   a.   15   b.   9   c.   30

   15 = _____   9 = _____   30 = _____

   Now use the prime factorizations from Problem 1 to answer Questions 2–4.

2. What is the least common multiple of 9 and 15? (*Hint:* If 9
   and 15 have any common prime factors, cross out one in
   each pair.)   _____

3. What is the least common multiple of 15 and 30?   _____

4. Add the following fractions. Use the factor trees in Problem 1 to help you find
   the least common denominators.

   a. $\frac{2}{15} = \frac{\boxed{}}{30}$ b. $\frac{4}{15} = \frac{\boxed{}}{\boxed{}}$ c. $\frac{2}{9} = \frac{\boxed{}}{\boxed{}}$

   $+ \frac{7}{30} = \frac{\boxed{}}{30}$ $+ \frac{1}{9} = \frac{\boxed{}}{\boxed{}}$ $+ \frac{1}{30} = \frac{\boxed{}}{\boxed{}}$

   _____   _____   _____

5. Use factor trees or some other method to find the least common denominator
   for $\frac{5}{14}$ and $\frac{2}{21}$.

   _____

Math Boxes 97

1. Alison's pizza has a radius of 8 inches.

> Circumference = π * d

a. Find the circumference of the pizza to the nearest inch.

_____

b. Find the area of the pizza to the nearest square inch.

_____

2. Solve.

Solution:

a. $49/e = 7$ _____

b. $240 = 8 * t$ _____

c. $r = \frac{640}{8}$ _____

d. $a = 187 - 38$ _____

e. $c - 705 = 428$ _____

3. Name a number between each pair of numbers.

a. 4.2 and 4.25   _____

b. $\frac{3}{8}$ and $\frac{3}{7}$ _____

c. −12 and −11   _____

d. $\frac{1}{10}$ and 0.15   _____

e. $\frac{2}{3}$ and $\frac{5}{6}$ _____

f. $\frac{7}{16}$ and $\frac{4}{5}$ _____

4. Complete the table. Graph the data and connect the points with line segments.

Maryanne earns $12 per hour.

Rule
Earnings = $12/hr * hours worked

hours	earnings
2	
4	
	60
	84
9	

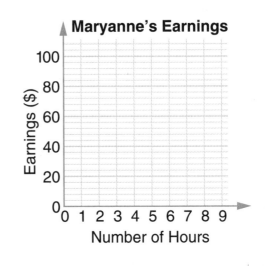

Maryanne's Earnings

School Days

Read the article "School" on pages 20–22 in the *American Tour Almanac*.

1. Tell whether the statement below is true or false. Support your answer with evidence from page 20 of the *American Tour Almanac*.

   In 1790, it was common for 11-year-olds to go to school fewer than 90 days a year.

   _____

   _____

   _____

2. About how many days will you go to school this year?   _____

   Write a fraction to compare the number of days you will go to school this year to the number of days an 11-year-old might have gone to school in 1790.   _____

3. Tell whether the statement below is true or false. Support your answer with evidence from page 21 of the *American Tour Almanac*.

   In 1900, students in some states spent twice as many days in school, on average, as students in some other states.

   _____

   _____

   _____

4. In 1900, in which region (Northeast, South, Midwest, or West) did students go to school

   the greatest number of days per year?   _____

   the fewest number of days per year?   _____

School Days (continued)

5. Tell whether the statement below is true or false. Support your answer with evidence from the graphs on page 22 of the *American Tour Almanac*.

   On average, students in 1980 were absent from school about one-half as many days as students were absent in 1900.

   _____

   _____

   _____

6. Tell whether the statement below is true or false. Support your answer with evidence from the *American Tour Almanac*.

   Almost all Americans believe that students should spend more time in school.

   _____

   _____

   _____

Challenge

7. Tell whether the statement below is true or false. Support your answer with evidence from the *American Tour Almanac*.

   From 1900 to 1980, the average number of days students spent in school per year more than doubled.

   _____

   _____

8. Locate your state in the table "Average Number of Days in School per Student, 1900" on page 21 of the *American Tour Almanac*.

   Was your state above or below the median for its region? _____
   (If you are in Alaska or Hawaii, choose another state.)

9. Locate the number of days in school for your state in the stem-and-leaf plot on page 21 of the *American Tour Almanac*.

   Was your state above or below the median for all states? _____

Use with Lesson 98.

A Short History of Mathematics Instruction

Throughout our nation's history, students have learned mathematics in different ways and have spent their time working on different kinds of problems. This is because people's views of what students can and should learn are constantly changing.

1. **1790s** If you went to elementary school in 1790, you were probably not taught mathematics. People believed that it was too hard to teach mathematics to children younger than 12.

   Older students spent most of their time solving problems about buying and selling goods. Here is a typical problem for a student in high school or college in the 1700s. Try to solve it.

   If 7 yards of cloth cost 21 shillings (a unit of money), how much do 19 yards of cloth cost? _____ shillings

2. **1840s** It was discovered that children could be very good at mental arithmetic, and students began to solve mental arithmetic problems as early as age 4. A school in Connecticut reported that its arithmetic champion could mentally multiply 314,521,325 by 231,452,153 in $5\frac{1}{2}$ minutes.

   After studying arithmetic two hours a day for 7 to 9 years, 94% of 8th graders in Boston in 1845 could solve the following problem. Try to solve it.

   What is $\frac{1}{2}$ of $\frac{1}{3}$ of 9 hours, 18 minutes? _____

3. **1870s** Many textbooks were step-by-step guides on how to solve various problems. Students were given problems and answers. They had to show how the rules in the textbook could be used to produce the given answers.

   Here is a problem from around 1870 (without the answer) given to students at the end of their 6 to 8 years of elementary arithmetic study. Try to solve it.

   I was married at the age of 21. If I live 19 years longer, I will have been married 60 years. What is my age now? _____

A Short History of Mathematics Instruction (continued)

4. **1920s** The emphasis in elementary mathematics was on developing skill with paper-and-pencil algorithms. The need for people to keep track of income, expenses, and profits for businesses was enormous, but there were no cheap, easy-to-use calculators. As a result, students spent much of their time doing exercises like the following. These problems are from a test for students in grades 5 through 8. Most students couldn't solve them until 7th grade. See how well you can do now (without a calculator).

$ 0.49	$ 8.00
0.28	5.75
0.63	2.33
0.95	4.16
1.69	0.94
0.22	+ 6.32
0.33	
0.36	
1.01	
+ 0.56	

5. **1990s** Today the emphasis is on solving problems and applying mathematics in the everyday world. The following problem was solved correctly by 47% of 8th graders on a test given in 1990. Try to solve it.

The cost to rent a motorbike is given by the following formula:

Cost = ($3 ∗ number of hours rented) + $2

Complete the following table:

Time	Cost
1 hr	$5
4 hr	$_____
_____ hr	$17

Use with Lesson 98.

Math Boxes 98

---

1. Circle the figure below that has the same area as Figure A.

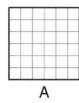

A

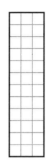 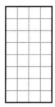

---

2. Add.

   a. 20 + (−10) = _____

   b. _____ = −8 + (−17)

   c. −12 + (−12) = _____

   d. _____ = −45 + 45

   e. _____ = −31 + 14

3. Divide or multiply mentally.

   a. 246/6 = _____

   b. 108/4 = _____

   c. 299 ∗ 15 = _____

   d. 35 ∗ 44 = _____

   e. 50 ∗ 27 = _____

---

4. Solve the pan-balance problems below.

   a.    

One △ weighs as much

as _____ X's.

One ⬡ weighs as much

as _____ X's.

   b.    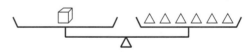

One ⬡ weighs as much

as _____ marbles.

One △ weighs as much

as _____ marbles.

Comparing Parts to Wholes

A **ratio** is a comparison. Some ratios compare part of a collection of things to the total number of things in the collection. For example, the statement "1 out of 6 students in the class is absent" compares the number of students absent to the total number of students in the class. Another way to express this ratio is to say, "For every 6 students enrolled in the class, 1 student is absent"; or, with a fraction: "$\frac{1}{6}$ of the students in the class are absent."

If you know the total number of students in the class, then you can use this ratio to find the number of students who are absent. For example, if there are 12 students in the class, then 2 of the students are absent. If there are 18 students in the class, then 3 students are absent.

If you know the number of students who are absent, then you can also use this ratio to find the total number of students in the class. For example, if 5 students are absent, then there must be a total of 30 students in the class.

Solve the following ratio problems. Use the square tiles you cut out from Activity Sheet 21 to help you.

1. Place 28 tiles on your desk so that 1 out of 4 tiles is white and the rest are shaded.

   How many tiles are white? _____

   How many tiles are shaded? _____

2. Place 30 tiles on your desk so that 4 out of 5 tiles are white and the rest are shaded.

   How many tiles are white? _____

   How many tiles are shaded? _____

3. Place 7 white tiles on your desk. Add some tiles so that 1 out of 3 tiles is white and the rest are shaded. How many tiles are there in all? _____

4. Place 25 white tiles on your desk. Add some tiles so that 5 out of 8 tiles are white and the rest are shaded. How many tiles are there in all? _____

5. Take 32 tiles. If 6 out of 8 are white, how many are white? _____

6. Take 15 tiles. If 6 out of 9 are white, how many are white? _____

7. Place 24 tiles on your desk so that 8 are white and the rest are shaded.

   One out of _____ tiles is white.

8. Place 18 tiles on your desk so that 12 are white and the rest are shaded.

   _____ out of 3 tiles are white.

Use with Lesson 99.

Ratio Number Stories

Use your tiles to model and solve the number stories below.

1. It rained 2 out of 5 days in the
    month of April. On how many days
    did it rain that month?

    _____

2. For every 4 times John was at bat,
    he got 1 hit. If he got 7 hits, how
    many times did he bat?

    _____

3. There are 20 students in Mrs.
    Kahlid's 5th grade class. Two out
    of 8 students have no brothers or
    sisters. How many students have
    no brothers or sisters?

    _____

4. Rema eats 2 eggs twice a week.
    How many eggs will she eat in the
    month of February?

    _____

    How many weeks will it take her to
    eat 32 eggs?

    _____

5. David took a survey of people's favorite flavors of ice cream. Of the people
    he surveyed, 2 out of 5 said that they like fudge swirl best, 1 out of 8 chose
    vanilla, 3 out of 10 chose maple walnut, and the rest chose another flavor.

    a. If 16 people said that fudge swirl is their favorite
        flavor, how many people took part in David's survey?   _____

    b. If 80 people participated in David's survey, how
        many preferred a flavor that is not fudge
        swirl, vanilla, or maple walnut?   _____

6. Make up your own ratio number story. Ask your partner to solve it.

    _____

    _____

    _____

    _____

    Answer: _____

Math Boxes 99

---

1.   **a.**   I am a polygon with exactly 4 angles, each of a different size. What shape am I?

_____

   b.   Draw what I might look like.

2.   Draw and label the following angles.

   a.   ∠*MNO:* 87° **b.**   ∠*DWB:* 155°

---

3.   Plot and label the ordered number pairs on the grid.

   M = (2,5)

   N = (−2,1)

   O = (−3,−4)

   P = (−4,3)

   Q = (6,−2)

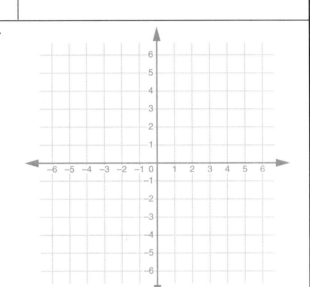

---

4.   Solve.

   a.   128.07
    − 85.25
    _____

   b.   18.95
    − 6.07
    _____

   c.   306.85
    + 216.96
    _____

   d.   147.09
    − 28.43
    _____

   e.   215.29
    + 38.75
    _____

   f.   463.17
    + 58.96
    _____

More Ratio Number Stories

You can solve ratio number stories by first writing a number model for the story.

Example

Sidney missed 2 out of 9 problems on the math test. There were 36 problems on the test. How many problems did he miss?

1. Write a number model: $\dfrac{\text{(missed) } 2}{\text{(total) } 9} = \dfrac{\square}{36}$

2. Find the missing number.

   Think: "9 times what number equals 36?" $9 * 4 = 36$

   Multiply the numerator, 2, by this number: $2 * 4 = 8$

   $$\frac{2 * 4}{9 * 4} = \frac{8}{36}$$

3. Answer: Sidney missed 8 out of 36 problems.

Write a number model for each problem. Then solve the problem.

1. Of the 42 animals in the Children's Zoo, 3 out of 7 are mammals. How many mammals are there in the Children's Zoo?

   Number model: _____   Answer: _____ mammals

2. Five out of 8 students at Kenwood School play an instrument. There are 224 students at the school. How many students play an instrument?

   Number model: _____   Answer: _____ students

3. Mr. Lopez sells subscriptions to a magazine. Each subscription costs $18. For each subscription he sells, he earns $8. One week, he sold $198 worth of subscriptions. How much did he earn?

   Number model: _____   Answer: $ _____

More Ratio Number Stories (continued)

4. There are 48 students in the 5th grade at Robert's school. Three out of
    8 fifth graders read two books last month. One out of 3 students read just
    one book. The rest of the students read no books at all.

    How many books in all did the 5th graders read last month? _____

    Explain what you did to find the answer. _____

    _____

    _____

5. Make up a ratio number story. Try to make it a hard one. Ask your partner to
    solve it.

    _____

    _____

    _____

    Answer: _____

Find the missing number.

6. $\frac{1}{3} = \frac{x}{39}$

    $x =$ _____

7. $\frac{3}{4} = \frac{21}{y}$

    $y =$ _____

8. $\frac{7}{8} = \frac{f}{56}$

    $f =$ _____

9. $\frac{1}{5} = \frac{13}{n}$

    $n =$ _____

10. $\frac{5}{6} = \frac{m}{42}$

    $m =$ _____

11. $\frac{9}{25} = \frac{s}{100}$

    $s =$ _____

Math Boxes 100

---

1. **a.** Which has the greater area, a 3-ft-by-2-ft rectangle or a triangle with base 3 ft and height 5 ft?

_____

   b. Which has the greater area, a triangle with base 10 cm and height 4 cm or a parallelogram with base 5 cm and height 6 cm?

_____

> Area of a rectangle $A = b * h$
>
> Area of a triangle $A = \frac{1}{2} * b * h$
>
> Area of a parallelogram $A = b * h$

---

2. Subtract.

   a. $10 - (-2) =$ _____

   b. $5 - 8 =$ _____

   c. $15 - (-5) =$ _____

   d. $-15 - (-5) =$ _____

   e. $-4 - 7 =$ _____

3. Divide or multiply mentally.

   a. $495/5 =$ _____

   b. $199 * 36 =$ _____

   c. $63 \times 500 =$ _____

   d. $25 * 96 * 4 =$ _____

   e. $843/3 =$ _____

---

4. Solve the pan-balance problems below.

a.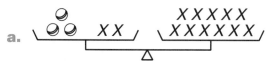

One ball weighs as much

as _____ X's.

One block weighs as much

as _____ X's.

b.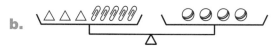

One △ weighs as much

as _____ paper clips.

One ball weighs as much

as _____ paper clips.

Using Video Data to Study Traffic and Driving Patterns

Traffic and highway engineers sometimes make videotapes of vehicles and drivers along a street or highway.

They use the videotapes to analyze vehicle speeds, traffic volume, and driving patterns. One driving pattern is the frequency with which drivers change lanes. Another is the tendency of drivers to form bunches or "packs" of vehicles along a stretch of open highway.

Videotape data help in making important decisions, such as the following:

- Where to locate traffic lights, stop signs, and warning signs
- What the speed limit should be
- How many lanes a new street or highway should have
- Whether lanes should be added to an existing highway

When Do Drivers Turn Their Headlights ON?

Mr. Wilson's 5th grade class wanted to know when drivers turn their headlights on as evening approaches. Do drivers turn their lights on at about the same time? Do almost all vehicles have their lights on at sunset?

The students decided to make a videotape of traffic. They selected a nearby street with moderately heavy traffic. They began taping after school, before it began to get dark.

The class made its videotape by taping 1-minute **traffic samples.**

1. Students taped traffic for exactly 1 minute.

2. Then they turned the camera off for exactly 3 minutes.

3. They repeated steps 1 and 2 until almost all vehicles had their lights on.

414   Use with Lesson 101.

When Do Drivers Turn Their Headlights ON? (continued)

1. If your class has a copy of the videotape Mr. Wilson's class made, your teacher will play it. For each 1-minute traffic sample, count the number of vehicles with headlights OFF and the number with headlights ON.

   If your class does not have the videotape, your teacher will give you a data table. Tape it over the first four columns of the table below.

   Your teacher will tell you how to complete the table.

	Beginning Time for 1-minute Sample	Vehicles with Lights OFF	Vehicles with Lights ON	Total Number of Vehicles	Fraction of Vehicles with Lights ON	Percent of Vehicles with Lights ON[1]
1	3:52 P.M.[2]	12	0	12	0/12	0%
2	3:56					
3	4:00					
4	4:04					
5	4:08					
6	4:12					
7	4:16					
8	4:20					
9	4:24					
10	4:28					
11	4:32					
12	4:36					
13	4:40					
14	4:44					
15	4:48[3]	0	15	15	15/15	100%

[1] Note: For each fraction $\frac{a}{b}$, use a calculator. First do $\frac{a}{b} * 100$. Then round your answer.

[2] Before 3:52 P.M., almost all vehicles had their headlights OFF.

[3] After 4:48 P.M., almost all vehicles had their headlights ON.

When Do Drivers Turn Their Headlights ON? (continued)

2. Make a graph to show the data for vehicles that had lights ON.

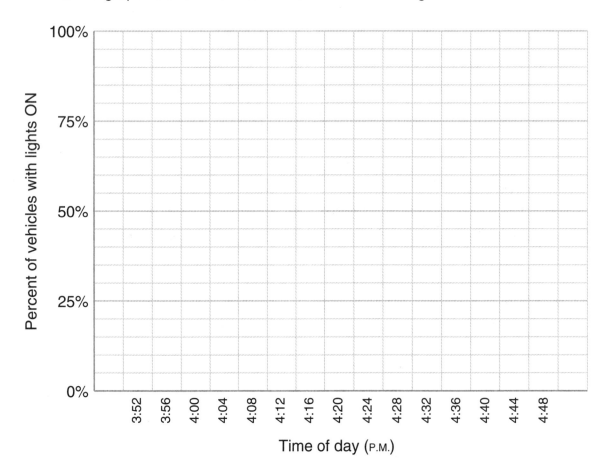

3. What percent of vehicles had their lights ON

   at 4:04 P.M.? _____%

   at 4:28 P.M.? _____%

4. Sunset was at 4:40 P.M. the day the videotape was made. Did almost all vehicles have their lights ON at sunset?

   _____

5. Find the first time for each event:

   a. At least 25% of vehicles had their lights ON. _____ P.M.

   b. At least 50% of vehicles had their lights ON. _____ P.M.

   c. At least 75% of vehicles had their lights ON. _____ P.M.

   d. At least 90% of vehicles had their lights ON. _____ P.M.

Math Boxes 101

1. Use your Geometry Template to trace three kinds of triangles in the space below. Under each triangle, write what kind of triangle it is.

2. Draw and label the following angles.

    a. ∠*FOG:* 43°   **b.** ∠*HAT:* 78°

3. Plot and label the ordered pairs on the grid at the right.

    E: (−2,5)

    F: (3,4)

    G: (−2,−4)

    H: (−1,0)

    I: (5,−1)

    J: (4,4)

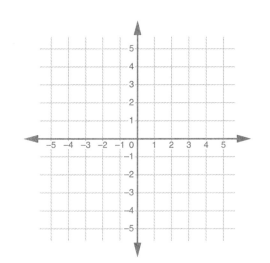

4. Subtract or add.

    a. $243.15 + 82.49 = $ _____

    b. $402.03 - 24.7 = $ _____

    c. $590.32 - 465.75 = $ _____

    d. _____ $ = 40.017 + 2.69$

    e. _____ $ = 24.303 + 5.7$

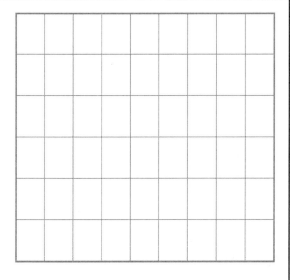

Time to Reflect

1. Describe one or two ways in which fractions and decimals are alike and one or two ways in which they are different.

_____

_____

_____

_____

_____

_____

_____

2. What is something that you enjoyed doing in this unit? Why did you enjoy that?

_____

_____

_____

_____

_____

_____

_____

_____

418

Math Boxes 102

---

1. Write 3 fractions equivalent to each fraction below.

   a. $\frac{3}{5}$ = _____

   b. $\frac{7}{8}$ = _____

   c. $\frac{2}{3}$ = _____

   d. $\frac{8}{9}$ = _____

   e. $\frac{1}{6}$ = _____

---

2. Write the fractions in order from greatest to least.

$$\frac{3}{8} \qquad \frac{9}{20} \qquad \frac{7}{15} \qquad \frac{9}{11} \qquad \frac{3}{5}$$

_____

_____

_____

_____

_____

---

3. Rename each pair of fractions with a common denominator.

   a. $\frac{2}{3}$ and $\frac{3}{4}$ _____

   b. $\frac{4}{6}$ and $\frac{7}{8}$ _____

   c. $\frac{3}{8}$ and $\frac{1}{7}$ _____

   d. $\frac{5}{9}$ and $\frac{5}{11}$ _____

   e. $\frac{6}{5}$ and $\frac{3}{10}$ _____

---

4. Add or subtract.

   a. $\frac{3}{8} + \frac{7}{4}$ = _____

   b. $\frac{5}{6} + \frac{1}{3}$ = _____

   c. $3\frac{3}{4} + \frac{2}{6}$ = _____

   d. $2\frac{1}{2} - \frac{3}{4}$ = _____

   e. $1\frac{7}{8} - \frac{1}{3}$ = _____

---

5. Write each fraction in simplest form.

   a. 6/36 = _____

   b. 14/21 = _____

   c. 81/9 = _____

   d. 27/8 = _____

   e. 25/35 = _____

---

6. Convert each of the following times to minutes.

   a. $\frac{1}{4}$ of an hour = _____min

   b. $\frac{3}{5}$ of an hour = _____min

   c. $\frac{5}{6}$ of an hour = _____min

   d. $\frac{7}{12}$ of an hour = _____min

   e. $\frac{2}{15}$ of an hour = _____min

Geometric Solids

A **geometric solid** is a 3-dimensional shape formed by surfaces. In spite of its name, a geometric solid is hollow, or empty. Its surfaces can be curved or flat.

The surfaces of a geometric solid meet in curves or on line segments. These curves or line segments are the **edges** of the solid.

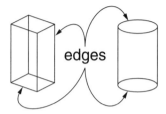

edges

 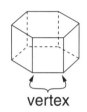

vertex

vertex

As with polygons, a "corner" of a geometric solid is called a **vertex** (plural *vertexes* or *vertices*). Edges meet at a vertex.

A **polyhedron** is a geometric solid whose surfaces are formed by polygons. These surfaces are the **faces** of the polyhedron. **Prisms** and **pyramids** are examples of polyhedrons.

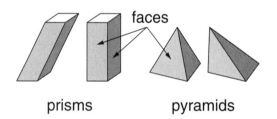

faces

prisms   pyramids

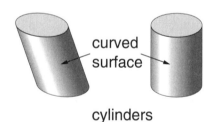

curved surface

cylinders

A **cylinder** has 3 surfaces: A flat "top" and a flat "bottom" formed by circles or ellipses, and a **curved surface** that connects them. The top and bottom are the faces of the cylinder.

A **cone** has 2 surfaces: A flat surface formed by a circle or ellipse and a curved surface that comes to a point.

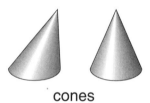

cones

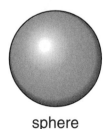

sphere

Like a circle, a **sphere** is the set of all the points that are the same distance from its center. But these are points in space, not just in one plane.

420

Geometric Solids (continued)

Each member of your group should cut out one of the patterns from Masters 73–76. Fold the pattern and glue or tape it together. Then add this model to your group's collection.

1. Examine your models of geometric solids.

   a. Which solids have all flat surfaces? _____

   _____

   b. Which have no flat surfaces? _____

   c. Which have both flat and curved surfaces? _____

   d. If you cut the label of a cylindrical can in a straight line perpendicular to the bottom, and then unrolled and flattened the label, what would be the shape of the label?

   _____

   cut line

2. Examine your models of polyhedrons.

   a. Which polyhedrons have more faces than vertices? _____

   b. Which have the same number of faces and vertices? _____

   _____

   c. Which have fewer faces than vertices? _____

   _____

3. Examine your model of a cube.

   a. Does it have more edges than vertices, the same number of edges as vertices, or fewer edges than vertices? _____

   Is this true for all polyhedrons? Explain. _____

   _____

   b. How many edges meet at each vertex? _____

   Is this true for all polyhedrons? Explain. _____

   _____

Use with Lesson 103.

Math Boxes 103

1. Complete the table.

Fraction	Decimal	Percent
$\frac{4}{5}$		
		35%
	0.7	
$\frac{8}{20}$		
		87.5%

2. Sheila runs a mile in the morning 5 days a week. How many weeks will it take her to run 45 miles?

_____

3. Solve the following problems mentally:

Solutions:

a. 458/7 →   _____

b. 399 * 40 =   _____

c. 2 × 83 × 50 =   _____

d. 48 * 15 =   _____

e. 793 ÷ 6 →   _____

4. Find the perimeter of each figure.

a. Perimeter:

_____

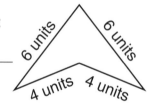

3 in   3 in
5 in   5 in
3 in

b. Perimeter:

_____

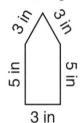

6 units   6 units
4 units   4 units

5. Measure each angle to the nearest degree.

a.

M

b.

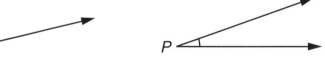

P

∠M measures about _____°.

∠P measures about _____°.

Use with Lesson 103.

Math Message: More about Geometric Solids

The faces (flat surfaces) of a cylinder are called its **bases.** Its bases are always opposite each other and parallel to each other.

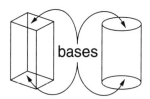

bases

Like cylinders, prisms have a pair of opposite, parallel bases. All edges that connect the bases of a prism must be parallel to each other.

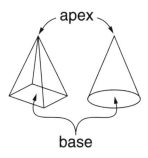

apex

base

Cones and pyramids each have exactly one base. The vertex opposite the base is called the **apex** of the cone or pyramid.

Spheres have no bases at all.

sphere

Prisms and pyramids are named after the shapes of their bases. For example, if the base of a pyramid has six sides, that solid would be a hexagonal pyramid.

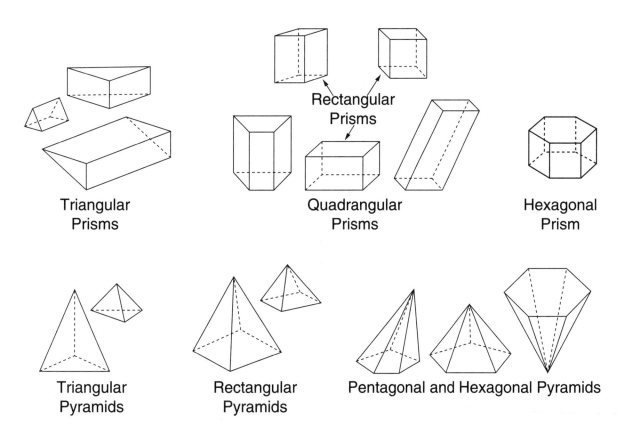

Rectangular Prisms

Triangular
Prisms

Quadrangular
Prisms

Hexagonal
Prism

Triangular
Pyramids

Rectangular
Pyramids

Pentagonal and Hexagonal Pyramids

Use with Lesson 104.

423

Math Message: More about Geometric Solids (continued)

Regular polyhedrons are made up of faces that are identical regular polygons. There are only five kinds of regular polyhedrons. As you can see, their faces can be only equilateral triangles, squares, or regular pentagons.

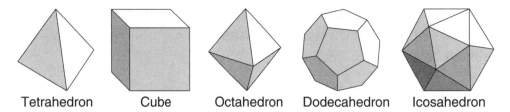

Tetrahedron   Cube   Octahedron   Dodecahedron   Icosahedron

What is one advantage of having dice that are regular polyhedrons?

_____

_____

_____

_____

Likenesses and Differences

1. How are prisms and pyramids alike?

_____

_____

_____

_____

What are some differences between prisms and pyramids?

_____

_____

_____

_____

Likenesses and Differences (continued)

2. How are prisms and cylinders alike?

_____

_____

_____

_____

What are some differences between prisms and cylinders?

_____

_____

_____

_____

_____

3. How are pyramids and cones alike?

_____

_____

_____

What are some differences between pyramids and cones?

_____

_____

_____

_____

_____

_____

Use with Lesson 104.

3-D Shape Sort

Materials ❑ 1 set of 12 cutout Shape cards from Activity Sheet 22
❑ 1 set of 16 Property cards from Activity Sheet 23

Number of players 2 (or 2 teams of 2 each)

Directions Spread out the Shape
cards on the playing surface, faceup.
Shuffle the Property cards and sort
them into two face-down piles,
Vertex/Edge cards and Surface cards.

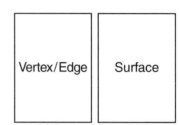

Players take turns doing the following:

1. Draw the top card from both
   piles of Property cards.

2. Take all the Shape cards that
   have both of the properties shown
   on the Property cards. For example,
   if a player draws cards that say
   "I have no vertices" and "I have
   at least one curved surface," he or she
   can take the cylinders and the sphere.

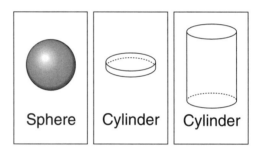

3. If there are no shapes with both properties, draw one additional Property
   card—either a Vertex/Edge card or a Surface card. Look for shapes that
   have the new property and one of the properties drawn previously. Take
   any Shape cards that match.

When all the Property cards have been drawn, shuffle the cards, sort them again
into two face-down piles, and continue playing.

If a player does not take a Shape card he or she could have taken, the other
player can take it.

The game ends when there are fewer than three Shape cards left. The player
with more Shape cards at the end of the game wins.

Math Boxes 104

---

1. Complete the table. Then graph the data and connect the points with line segments.

David rides his bike at a speed of about 12 miles per hour.

Rule
12 * number of hours = total miles

in	out
1	12
2	
	36
	42
5	

David's Bike Speed

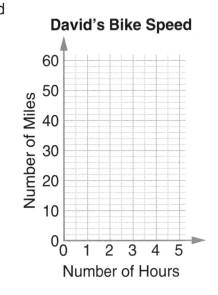

Number of Miles (vertical axis): 0, 10, 20, 30, 40, 50, 60

Number of Hours (horizontal axis): 0 1 2 3 4 5

---

2. Will a circle with an area of 28 square centimeters fit inside a circle with a radius of 5 centimeters? _____ Explain your answer.

_____

_____

_____

_____

_____

_____

_____

3. Draw a picture of 18 tiles so that 2 out of 3 are shaded.

---

4. Mark and label each point on the ruler below.

$A: 4\frac{1}{4}$ in $B: \frac{3}{16}$ in $C: 2\frac{7}{8}$ in $D: 1\frac{1}{2}$ in $E: 3\frac{3}{8}$ in

| 1 | 2 | 3 | 4 | 5 |

INCHES

Math Message: What Is Volume?

The **volume** of a geometric solid, such as a box, a brick, or a ball, is a measure of how much space the solid takes up, or of how much material it would take to fill it. The volume of a container that can be filled with a liquid, such as a milk bottle or a gas tank, is the measure of how much liquid the container will hold. The volume of such a container is often called its **capacity.**

Volume is measured in **cubic units,** such as cubic inches (in^3), cubic feet (ft^3), and cubic centimeters (cm^3). It is easy to find the volumes of objects that are shaped like cubes or other rectangular prisms. For example, a container in the shape of a 10-cm cube (that is, a cube that is 10 cm by 10 cm by 10 cm) can be filled with exactly 1000 centimeter cubes. Therefore, the volume of a 10-cm cube is 1000 cubic centimeters (1000 cm^3), and its capacity is 1 liter.

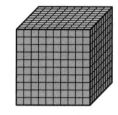

1 cm^3 1000 cm^3

It is not always possible to fill a container with unit cubes to find its volume. The explorations in this unit will show you how to find the volumes of rectangular prisms and other solids—such as triangular prisms, pyramids, cylinders, cones, and spheres—by measuring their linear **dimensions.** You will learn that it is even possible to find the volumes of objects whose dimensions cannot be measured, such as rocks or parts of your own body.

The Dimensions of
a Rectangular Prism

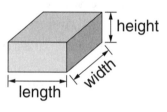

Examine the patterns on Activity Sheet 25. These patterns are used to construct open boxes—boxes that have no tops. Try to figure out how many centimeter cubes are needed to fill each box to the top. Do not cut out the patterns.

1. I think that _____ centimeter cubes are needed to fill Box A to the top.

2. I think that _____ centimeter cubes are needed to fill Box B to the top.

3. Explain how you found the number of cubic centimeters needed to fill Box B to the top.

_____

_____

_____

          Use with Lesson 105.

Volumes of Rectangular Prisms

Write the formula for the volume of a rectangular prism.

_____

B is the area of the base.

h is the height from that base.

V is the volume of the prism.

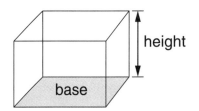

Find the volume of each rectangular prism below.

1.

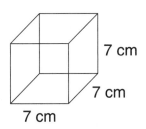

5 in

4 in

4 in

V = _____

2.

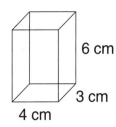

6 cm

3 cm

4 cm

V = _____

3.

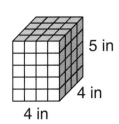

7 cm

7 cm

7 cm

V = _____

4.

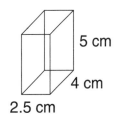

5 cm

4 cm

2.5 cm

V = _____

5.

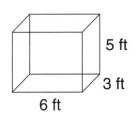

5 ft

3 ft

6 ft

V = _____

6.

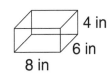

4 in

6 in

8 in

V = _____

Math Boxes 105

---

1. Rename each fraction as a mixed number or a whole number.

a. $\frac{79}{8}$ = _____

b. $\frac{45}{9}$ = _____

c. $\frac{111}{3}$ = _____

d. $\frac{126}{6}$ = _____

e. $\frac{108}{5}$ = _____

2. Solve.

Solutions:

a. $-12 + d = -14$ _____

b. $28 - e = -2$ _____

c. $b + 18 = -24$ _____

d. $-14 = f - 7$ _____

e. $12 = 16 + g$ _____

---

3. Mrs. Porter's students took a survey of their favorite movie snacks. Complete the table. Then make a circle graph of the data.

Favorite Snack	Number of Students	Percent of Class
Popcorn	11	
Chocolate	5	
Soft Drink	6	
Fruit Chews	2	
Candy w/ Nuts	1	
Total		

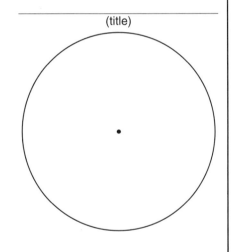

(title)

---

4. Use your calculator to complete the table.

Exponential Notation	Product of Factors	Standard Notation
4^4		
	$5 * 5 * 5$	
6^4		1296
	$7 * 7 * 7 * 7 * 7$	
9^3		

5. Add or subtract.

a. $2\frac{5}{9} - 1\frac{7}{8}$ = _____

b. _____ = $\frac{42}{4} - 2\frac{2}{3}$

c. _____ = $3\frac{8}{12} - 2\frac{11}{12}$

d. _____ = $4\frac{8}{5} + 2\frac{3}{7}$

e. _____ = $\frac{32}{12} + 3\frac{2}{3}$

430

Metric Units of Volume and Capacity

The **cubic centimeter (cm^3)** is a metric unit of volume.

The **liter (L)** and **milliliter (mL)** are metric units of capacity.

1. Complete: 1 liter (L) = _____ milliliters (mL)

2. Calculate the volume of your 5-cm cube container.

    Volume = _____ cubic centimeters

3. Fill your 5-cm cube with rice, sand, or sugar.

    a. First, fill it to overflowing.
        Then, lay an index card flat
        on top of the cube. Slide the
        card back and forth until the
        cube is filled—level and to
        the top.

    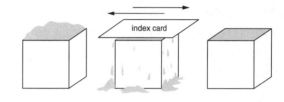

    b. Pour the cube's contents into a measuring cup.

    c. Shake the material in the cup until it is level.

    d. Fill the cube a second time. Then pour the contents
        into the measuring cup—and shake the material in the
        cup until it is level. How many cubic centimeters
        of material are in the measuring cup now?   _____ cm^3

    e. How many milliliters of material are in the cup?   _____ mL

4. How many cubic centimeters do you think there are in 1 liter?   _____ cm^3

    Explain your answer.

    _____

    _____

    _____

    _____

Metric Units of Volume and Capacity (continued)

5. How many cubic centimeters of material do you think it would take to fill your 5-cm cube container to the 1-cm level? _____ cm³

To check your answer, fill your measuring cone with that amount of material. Pour it into the cube. Shake the cube to make the material level.

Does the material reach the 1-cm level? _____

6. How many cubic centimeters of material do you think you would have to add in order to fill your cube to the very top? _____ cm³

To check your answer, use your measuring cone to fill the cube with that amount of material.

Don't remove the material already in the cube. Shake the cube to make the material level.

Is the cube completely filled? _____

7. Do you think the measuring cone is accurate? _____ Why or why not?

_____

_____

_____

61 Seconds in a Minute?
When the only clocks were mechanical, the definition of a second was 1/86,400 of a solar day. Now there are atomic clocks, which are far more accurate. A second is defined as the time it takes for a cesium atom (under specific temperature and pressure conditions) to vibrate 9,192,631,770 times.

By this new standard, Earth falls behind every now and then. For this reason, scientists add an extra second to the year while Earth catches up. The first second was added in June 1972. Since then, about 20 seconds have been added.

Math Boxes 106

---

1. Complete the table.

Fraction	Decimal	Percent
	0.18	
		37.5%
$\frac{45}{50}$		
$\frac{16}{25}$		
	0.88	

2. Ben made a basket on 3 out of every 5 attempts. If he took 30 shots, how many baskets did he make?

_____

---

3. Solve the following problems mentally:

Solutions:

a. What is $\frac{1}{3}$ of 210? _____

b. $\frac{809}{5} \rightarrow$ _____

c. $25 * 88 =$ _____

d. $60 * 899 =$ _____

e. $576/9 =$ _____

4. Find the perimeter of each figure.

a. _____

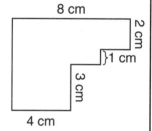

8 cm
2 cm
}1 cm
3 cm
4 cm

b. _____

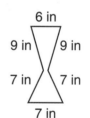

6 in
9 in   9 in
7 in   7 in
7 in

---

5. Measure each angle to the nearest degree.

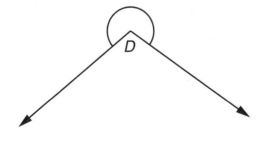

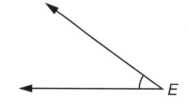

a. ∠D measures about _____°.   **b.** ∠E measures about _____°.

Math Message: Volumes of Prisms

The structures below are made up of centimeter cubes.

1.

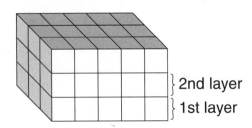

Area of base = _____ cm²

Volume of 1st layer = _____ cm³

Volume of prism = _____ cm³

2.

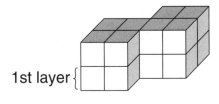

Area of base = _____ cm²

Volume of 1st layer = _____ cm³

Volume of prism = _____ cm³

3.

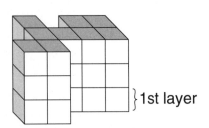

Area of base = _____ cm²

Volume of 1st layer = _____ cm³

Volume of prism = _____ cm³

4.

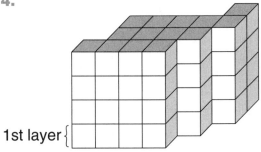

Area of base = _____ cm²

Volume of 1st layer = _____ cm³

Volume of prism = _____ cm³

Volumes of Prisms

1. Use Pattern A1 on Activity Sheet 28 or Pattern C1 on Activity Sheet 29 to construct a triangular prism.

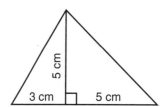

2. Circle the figure at the right that shows the base of your triangular prism.

What is the area of the base? _____ cm²

3. Pour material into your triangular prism to the 1-cm level. Then pour it into your measuring cone. What is the approximate volume of the material? _____ cm³

4. How many cubic centimeters of material do you think you will need to fill your triangular prism to the very top? _____ cm³

Why do you think so? _____

_____

_____

Use your measuring cone to check your answer.

5. Find the volume of each prism below.

a.

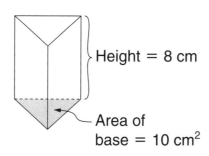

Height = 8 cm

Area of base = 10 cm²

Volume = _____ cm³

b.

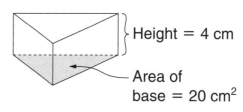

Height = 4 cm

Area of base = 20 cm²

Volume = _____ cm³

Volumes of Prisms (continued)

6. Use Pattern B1 on Activity Sheet 28 or Pattern D1 on Activity Sheet 29
   to construct a 4-sided prism.

7. Circle the figure at the right that shows
   the base of your 4-sided prism.

   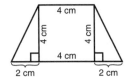

   (Think of this figure
   as being composed
   of 2 triangles.)

   What is the area of the base? _____ cm²

8. Pour material into your 4-sided prism to the 1-cm level.
   Then pour it into your measuring cone.

   What is the approximate volume of the material?   _____ cm³

9. How many total cubic centimeters of material do you think
   will be needed to fill your 4-sided prism to the very top?   _____ cm³

   Use your measuring cone to check your answer.

10. How would you calculate the volume of this prism?

    _____

    _____

11. Could you use your method to calculate the volume of any prism?

12. Find the volume of each prism below.

    a.

    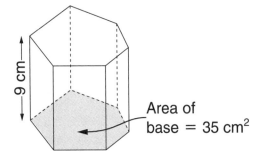

    Volume = _____ cm³

    b.

    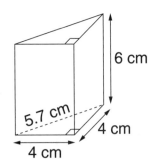

    Volume = _____ cm³

> **Summary:** For any prism, the volume can be found using the
> formula $V = B * h$, where B is the area of the base and h is the
> height perpendicular to that base.

Open Boxes

What are the dimensions of an open box—having the greatest possible volume—that can be made out of a single sheet of centimeter grid paper?

Use centimeter grid paper to experiment until you discover a pattern. Record your results in the table below.

Height of Box	Length of Base	Width of Base	Volume of Box
1 cm	20 cm	14 cm	
2 cm			
3 cm			

What are the dimensions of the box with the greatest volume?

Height of box = _____ cm   Length of base = _____ cm

Width of base = _____ cm   Volume of box = _____ cm^3

Math Boxes 107

1. Complete the table. Then graph the data and connect the points with line segments.

   Robin runs $\frac{1}{2}$ mile in 4 minutes.

Rule
$\frac{1}{8}$ * number of minutes = total miles

minutes	total miles
4	$\frac{1}{2}$
8	
	2
	$3\frac{1}{2}$
32	

   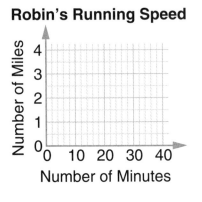

2. Will a circle with an area of 20 square centimeters fit inside a circle with a diameter of 4 centimeters? _____
   Explain your answer.

   _____

   _____

   _____

   _____

   _____

   _____

   _____

3. Draw 12 shaded tiles. Then draw some unshaded tiles so that 3 out of 5 tiles are shaded.

4. Mark and label each point on the ruler below.

   A: $3\frac{3}{8}$"   *B:* $1\frac{5}{16}$"   *C:* $\frac{15}{16}$"   *D:* $4\frac{5}{8}$"   *E:* $2\frac{3}{4}$"

   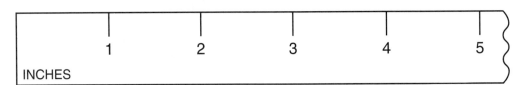

Use with Lesson 107.

Comparing Populations

Compare the Number of People 5–14 Years Old with the Number of People 65 Years Old or Older, 1850–2020

Working with your classmates, use the information in the table at the bottom of page 23 of the *American Tour Almanac* to complete the following three displays:

Display 1: Line Graph

Number of People 5–14 Years Old and People 65 Years Old or Older, 1850–2020

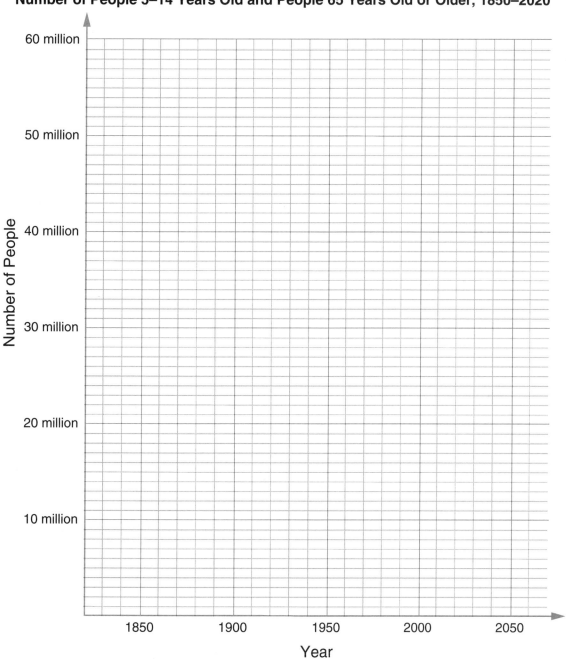

Key: ▲ People 5–14 Years Old ■ People 65 Years Old or Older

Comparing Populations (continued)

Display 2: Ratio Table

First, compare the number of people 5–14 years old with the number of people 65 years old or older. Then make a comparison with 1 (round to the nearest tenth).

In 1850:   _6,060,000_ to _575,000_   _10.5_ to _1_

In 1900:   _____ to _____   _____ to _____

In 1950:   _____ to _____   _____ to _____

In 2000 (predicted):   _____ to _____   _____ to _____

In 2020 (predicted):   _____ to _____   _____ to _____

Display 3: Percent Bars

Percent of the Total Population

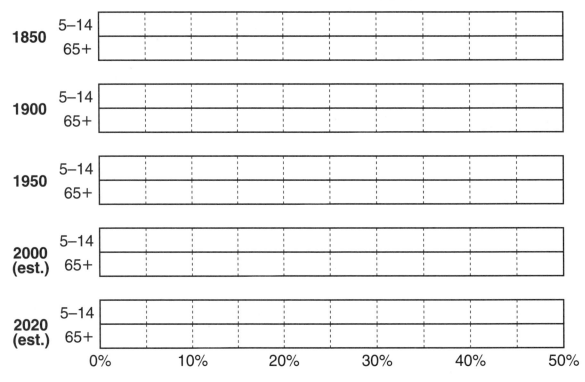

Living to 100

Examine the bar graph and the line graph at the bottom of page 24 in the *American Tour Almanac.* They show the same data but display them in different ways.

1. What do these graphs tell us about the number of people 100 years old and older?

_____

_____

_____

2. Which seems easier to read and use—the bar graph or the line graph? Why?

_____

_____

3. During which period will the number of people 100 years old and older nearly double?

_____

4. During which period will there be the greatest increase in the number of people 100 years old and older?

_____

5. If you live to age 100, what year will it be?

_____

6. Why do you think the number of people 100 years old and older has increased at such a fast rate?

_____

_____

7. What advantages and disadvantages are there for our society having more people 100 years old and older?

_____

_____

Math Boxes 108

---

1. Rename each fraction as a mixed number or a whole number.

a. $\frac{59}{5}$ = _____

b. $\frac{88}{11}$ = _____

c. $\frac{120}{7}$ = _____

d. $\frac{94}{4}$ = _____

e. $\frac{102}{6}$ = _____

2. Solve.

Solutions:

a. $6 = 20 + s$ _____

b. $18 + t = -2$ _____

c. $-15 + u = -23$ _____

d. $-11 - v = -5$ _____

e. $29 - w = 35$ _____

---

3. The students in Ms. Dillard's class took a survey of their favorite colors. Complete the table. Then make a circle graph of the data.

Favorite Color	Number of Students	Percent of Class
Red	6	
Blue	10	
Orange	4	
Yellow	2	
Purple	3	
Total		

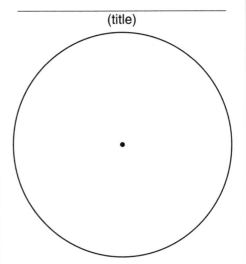

_____
(title)

---

4. Use your calculator to complete the table.

Exponential Notation	Product of Factors	Standard Notation
9^4		
	12 * 12 * 12 * 12	20,736
8^4		
	11 * 11 * 11 * 11 * 11	
10^3		

5. Add or subtract.

a. $\frac{3}{8} + \frac{9}{2}$ = _____

b. $\frac{11}{12} + 3\frac{4}{5}$ = _____

c. $2\frac{4}{3} - \frac{7}{8}$ = _____

d. $4\frac{2}{5} - 2\frac{5}{6}$ = _____

e. $5\frac{3}{4} + 2\frac{5}{12}$ = _____

Volumes of Cylinders

> **Formula for the Area of a Circle**
>
> $$A = \pi * r^2$$
>
> where A is the area and r the radius of the circle.

1. Choose a can and find its volume by using your 5-cm cube container and measuring cone to fill the can. Keep track of the total amount of material you pour into the can.

   The volume of the can is about

   _____ cm^3.

2. Choose a second can and find its volume in the same way.

   The volume of this can is about

   _____ cm^3.

The formula for finding the volume of a cylinder is the same as the formula for finding the volume of a prism.

> **Formula for the Volume of a Cylinder**
>
> $$V = B * h$$
>
> where V is the volume of the cylinder, B is the area of the base, and h is the height of the cylinder.

3. Measure the height of each can, inside the can. Measure the diameter of the base of each can. Record your measurements (to the nearest tenth of a centimeter) in the table below.

4. Calculate the radius of the base of each can. Then use the formula to find the volume. Record the results in the table.

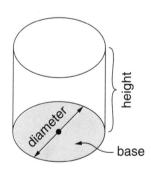

5. Record the capacity of each can in the table, in milliliters.

	Height (cm)	Diameter of Base (cm)	Radius of Base (cm)	Volume (cm³)	Capacity (mL)
Can #1					
Can #2					

Volumes of Cylinders (continued)

6. Find the volume of each cylinder.

a.

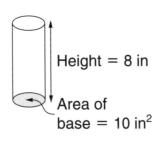

Height = 8 in

Area of
base = 10 in²

b.

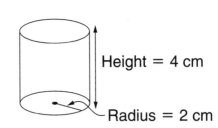

Height = 4 cm

Radius = 2 cm

Volume = _____ in³   Volume = _____ cm³

Challenge

7. Think: How would you find the **area** of all the metal used to manufacture a can?

a. How would you find the area of the top or bottom of the can?

_____

_____

_____

b. How would you find the area of the curved surface between the top and
bottom of the can?

_____

_____

_____

c. Choose a can. Find the total area of the metal used to manufacture the can.

Area of top = _____

Area of bottom = _____

Area of curved side surface = _____

Total area = _____

Use with Lesson 109.

Math Boxes 109

---

1. If a set has 48 objects, how many objects are there in

a. $\frac{3}{8}$ of the set? _____

b. $\frac{8}{3}$ of the set ? _____

c. $\frac{5}{6}$ of the set ? _____

d. $\frac{7}{12}$ of the set ? _____

e. $\frac{17}{16}$ of the set ? _____

2. Add or subtract.

a. $3\frac{4}{5} - 1\frac{7}{8} =$ _____

b. $\frac{15}{12} - 1\frac{1}{8} =$ _____

c. $\frac{22}{7} - 2\frac{2}{3} =$ _____

d. $\frac{5}{6} + 2\frac{3}{4} =$ _____

e. $4\frac{1}{3} + 3\frac{2}{8} =$ _____

---

3. Solve.

a.
```
    3.26
+ 504.1
_____
```

b.
```
  793.82
+ 409.785
_____
```

c.
```
  987.55
+ 283.6
_____
```

d.
```
   52.6
- 19.08
_____
```

e.
```
  703.93
- 251.09
_____
```

d.
```
  826.3
- 572.91
_____
```

---

4. Find the area of each figure.

Area of a triangle: $A = \frac{1}{2} * b * h$ Area of a parallelogram: $A = b * h$

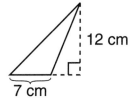

12 cm

7 cm

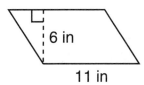

6 in

11 in

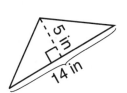

5 in

14 in

a. Area: _____   **b.** Area: _____   **c.** Area: _____

Volumes of Pyramids and Cones

A. Make pyramids that fit your prisms.

1. Look at the triangular and 4-sided prisms you constructed in Lesson 107, and find the circled letters on the bases.

2. On Activity Sheet 30, use the patterns that have the same circled letters as the letters on your prisms (for example, A1 and A2).

3. Cut out the two shapes along the solid lines. Score along the dashed lines.

4. Fold along the dashed lines to form a pyramid.

5. Tape the edges where the sides join. Tape along the entire edge.

B. Make a cone that fits your can.

1. Measure the distance from the center of the base of the can to the top rim.

2. Open your compass to this same length, and then open it about $\frac{1}{2}$ inch more.

3. Draw a semicircle (half of a circle) on a sheet of paper. Cut out the semicircle.

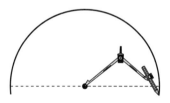

4. Roll the cutout semicircle to make a cone. Put a small piece of tape at the tip (apex) of the cone to help maintain its shape.

5. Place the cone in the can so that the tip of the can touches the base of the can.

6. Spread out the cone so that it fills out the can at the top. Tape the inside of the cone so that it keeps its shape.

7. Draw a line on the inside of the cone where the cone touches the rim of the can.

Volumes of Pyramids and Cones (continued)

1. Use your triangular prism and triangular pyramid.

    a. Fill the pyramid so that the material is level with the top.
    Empty the material into the prism.

    b. Fill the pyramid again and empty the material into the prism.

    c. Repeat until the prism is full to the top.

    d. It takes about _____ pyramids of material to fill the prism.

2. Use your 4-sided prism and 4-sided pyramid.

    a. Repeat the steps in Problem 1.

    b. It takes about _____ pyramids of material to fill the prism.

3. Use your can and the cone you just made.

    a. Fill the cone to the level shown by your pencil mark.
    Empty the material into the can.

    b. Fill the cone again and empty the material into the can.

    c. Repeat until the can is filled to the top.

    d. It takes about _____ cones of material to fill the can.

4. To calculate the volume of any **prism** or **cylinder,** you multiply the area
   of the base by the height. How would you calculate the volume of a
   pyramid or **cone**?

   _____

   _____

   _____

   _____

Math Boxes 110

1. Solve.

a. $\frac{1}{2}$ of 12 = _____

b. $\frac{2}{3}$ of 18 = _____

c. $\frac{3}{8}$ of 24 = _____

d. $\frac{6}{9}$ of 30 = _____

e. $\frac{1}{2}$ of $\frac{1}{2}$ = _____

2. Round each number to the nearest tenth.

a. 50.009 _____

b. 321.65 _____

c. 2.38 _____

d. 0.09 _____

e. 75.993 _____

3. Multiply or divide.

a. $389 * 520 =$ _____

b. _____ $= 2099 * 37$

c. $2435/49 \rightarrow$ _____

d. $856/84 \rightarrow$ _____

e. _____ $= 492 * 123$

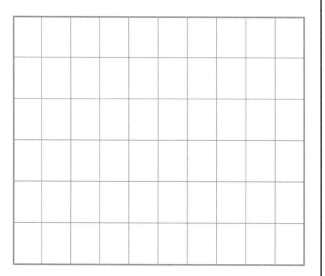

4. Solve.

a.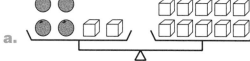

One orange weighs as much

as _____ X's.

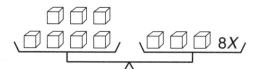

One cube weighs as much

as _____ X's.

b.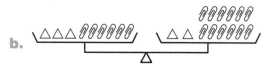

One triangle weighs as much

as _____ X's.

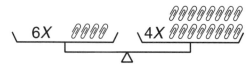

One paper clip weighs as much

as _____ X's.

Use with Lesson 110.

How to Calibrate a Bottle

Materials   ☐ 2-liter plastic soft-drink bottle with the top cut off
                  ☐ measuring cup   ☐ ruler
                  ☐ scissors   ☐ paper
                  ☐ tape   ☐ can or jar filled with about
                                        2 liters of water

1. Fill the bottle with about 5 inches of water.

2. Cut a 1"-by-6" strip of paper. Tape the strip to the outside of the bottle with one end at the bottle top and the other end below the water level.

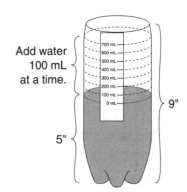

3. Mark the paper strip at the water level. Write "0 mL" next to the mark.

4. Pour 100 milliliters of water into a measuring cup. Pour the water into the bottle. Mark the paper strip at the new water level and write "100 mL."

5. Pour another 100 milliliters of water into the measuring cup. Pour it into the bottle and mark the new water level "200 mL."

6. Repeat, adding 100 milliliters at a time until the bottle is filled to within an inch of the top.

7. Pour out the water until the water level in the bottle falls to the 0-mL mark.

Finding Volume by a Displacement Method

How would you use your calibrated bottle to find the volume of a rock?

_____

_____

_____

_____

_____

_____

Finding Volume by a Displacement Method (continued)

> *Reminder:* 1 mL = 1 cm^3

1. Check that the bottle is filled to the 0-mL level. Place several rocks in the bottle.

   a. What is the new level of the water in the bottle? _____ mL

   b. What is the volume of the rocks? _____ cm^3

   c. Does it matter whether the rocks are spread out or stacked? _____

2. Your fist has nearly the same volume as your heart. Here is a way to find the approximate volume of your heart. Check that the bottle is filled to the 0-mL level. Place a rubber band around your wrist, just below your wrist bone. Put your fist in the bottle until water reaches the rubber band.

   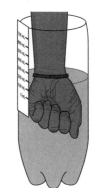

   a. What is the new level of the water in the bottle? _____ mL

   b. What is the volume of your fist? This is the approximate volume of your heart. _____ cm^3

   c. Does it matter whether you make a fist or keep your hand open? _____

3. Find the volumes of several other objects in the same way. For example, find the volume of a baseball, a tennis ball, an orange, a banana, or a full can of a soft drink. If the object floats in water, use a pencil to force it down. The object must be completely submerged before you read the water level.

Object	Volume of Water Object Displaces (mL)	Volume of Object (cm^3)

                                                       Use with Lesson 111.

Math Boxes 111

1. **a.** $\frac{5}{7}$ of a set contains 25 objects. How many objects are in the whole set? _____

   b. $\frac{4}{9}$ of a set contains 36 objects. How many objects are in the whole set? _____

   c. $\frac{11}{12}$ of a set contains 88 objects. How many objects are in the whole set? _____

2. Add or subtract.

   a. $\frac{3}{8} + 1\frac{2}{3} =$ _____

   b. $\frac{5}{6} + \frac{3}{4} =$ _____

   c. $\frac{7}{8} - \frac{1}{2} =$ _____

   d. $1\frac{5}{9} - \frac{2}{3} =$ _____

   e. $\frac{19}{12} - \frac{6}{8} =$ _____

3. Add or subtract.

   a. $384.06 + 207.9 =$ _____

   b. _____ $= 78.054 + 3.999$

   c. _____ $= 204.36 - 187.09$

   d. _____ $= 63.5 - 17.084$

   e. _____ $= 237 - 3.87$

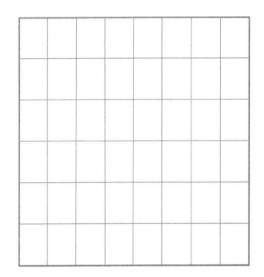

4. Find the area of each figure.

> Area of a triangle: $A = \frac{1}{2} * b * h$ Area of a parallelogram: $A = b * h$

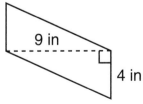
9 in
4 in

16 cm
9 cm

15 yd
8 yd

   a. Area: _____   **b.** Area: _____   **c.** Area: _____

Walkers' Speed and Length of Steps

How Fast Do People Walk, and What Is the Length of Walkers' Steps?

The video that you will watch shows people of all ages, who were filmed walking between two marker poles. The poles are set exactly $\frac{1}{100}$ mile (52.8 feet) apart.

Each walker is first shown at normal speed, and then shown again repeating the same walk at exactly $\frac{1}{2}$ speed. Use a stopwatch to time the first walk between the poles. Time to the nearest $\frac{1}{10}$ second. (If several students time the walk, use the median time.)

Then use the second walk at $\frac{1}{2}$ speed to count the number of steps the person takes to cover the distance between the poles. Round to the nearest whole number of steps (no fractions).

If your class does not use the videotape, your teacher will give you a table with walking data. Cut out the table and tape it in the space below.

Walker	Number of Steps	Time to the Nearest $\frac{1}{10}$ Sec	Time to the Nearest $\frac{1}{2}$ Sec
1			
2			
3			
4			
5			
6			
7			
8	Do not use: jogging		
9			
10			
11			

Walker	Number of Steps	Time to the Nearest $\frac{1}{10}$ Sec	Time to the Nearest $\frac{1}{2}$ Sec
12			
13			
14			
15	Do not use: walking dog		
16			
17			
18			
19	Do not use: stilts		
20			
21			
22			

How Fast Do People Walk?

1. Use the walking-time data to make a bar graph or a line plot.

bar graph

line plot

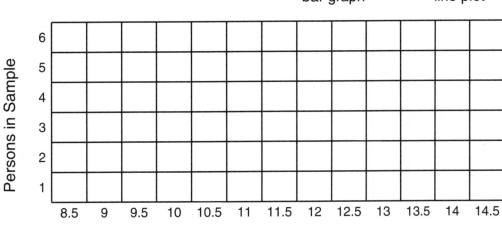

Time (in Seconds) to Cover 1/100 Mile (52.8 Feet)

2. Use the graph or plot to find these landmarks:

   maximum time: _____ seconds   minimum time: _____ seconds

   median time: _____ seconds   **modal** time: _____ seconds

3. Complete the table below.

Speed in mph (miles per hour)	Minutes for 1 Mile	Seconds for 1 Mile	Seconds for $\frac{1}{100}$ Mile (= 52.8 feet)
2 mph	30 min	30 * 60 = 1800 sec	$\frac{1800}{100}$ = 18 sec
3 mph	20 min	20 * 60 = 1200 sec	$\frac{1200}{100}$ = 12 sec
4 mph	15 min	sec	sec
5 mph	min	sec	sec
6 mph	min	sec	sec

4. A median walker (see Problem 2) walks at a pace of about _____ mph.

Challenge

5. The slowest walker walks at a pace of about _____ mph.

What Is the Length of Walkers' Steps?

1. Use the number-of-steps data to make a bar graph or a line plot.

bar graph

line plot

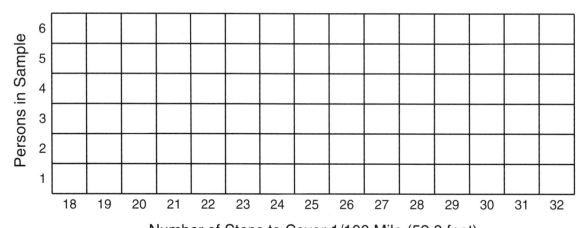

Persons in Sample

18   19   20   21   22   23   24   25   26   27   28   29   30   31   32

Number of Steps to Cover 1/100 Mile (52.8 feet)

2. Use the graph or plot to find these landmarks:

maximum number of steps: _____   minimum number of steps: _____

median number of steps: _____   **modal** number of steps: _____

3. Complete the table below.

Number of Steps to Cover 52.8 Feet ($\frac{1}{100}$ mile)	Length of One Step (Use a calculator. Round to tenths.)	
18 steps	52.8 ft / 18 steps =	2.9 feet
19 steps	52.8 ft / 19 steps =	2.8 feet
20 steps	52.8 ft / 20 steps =	feet
21 steps		feet
22 steps		feet
25 steps		feet
30 steps		feet

4. A median walker (see Problem 2) has a step length of about _____ feet.

5. The maximum walker (see Problem 2) has a step length of about _____ feet.

454

Math Boxes 112

---

1. Solve.

a. $\frac{4}{5}$ of 25 = _____

b. $\frac{5}{7}$ of 35 = _____

c. $\frac{3}{12}$ of 16 = _____

d. $\frac{6}{8}$ of 20 = _____

e. $\frac{1}{2}$ of $\frac{1}{4}$ = _____

2. Round each number to the nearest hundred.

a. 318,495.1 _____

b. 79,002 _____

c. 604,381 _____

d. 13,229 _____

e. 5,098 _____

---

3. Multiply or divide.

a. 2455/18 → _____

b. 3982/36 → _____

c. 1719 ÷ 56 → _____

d. 7512
   ∗ 483
   _____

e. 824
   × 137
   _____

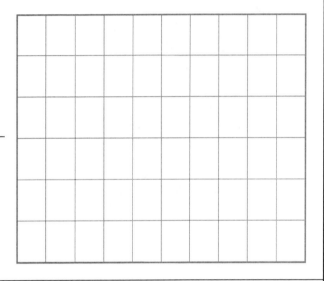

---

4. Solve.

a.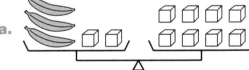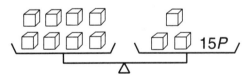

One banana weighs as much

as _____ P's.

One block weighs as much

as _____ P's.

b.

One block weighs as much

as _____ marbles.

One X weighs as much

as _____ marbles.

Time to Reflect

1. For each shape named below, try to think of 2 or 3 everyday objects that have this shape. These may be objects you see around your house, on your way to school, or anywhere else. The first one has been started for you.

    a. Cylinder: *coffee can* _____ _____

    b. Rectangular prism: _____ _____ _____

    c. Sphere: _____ _____ _____

    d. Cone: _____ _____ _____

2. Tell whether you agree or disagree with each statement below. If you disagree, explain why.

    a. A penny is shaped like a cylinder.

    _____

    _____

    _____

    b. A pear is shaped like a sphere.

    _____

    _____

    _____

    c. Many pencils are hexagonal prisms.

    _____

    _____

    _____

3. Tell what is meant by the volume of a 3-dimensional figure. Pretend that you are trying to explain it to a new student.

    _____

    _____

    _____

Math Boxes 113

1. Each face of a cube has an area of 25 square inches. What is the volume of the cube?

_____

2. The prism below is made of centimeter cubes.

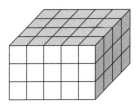

a. What is the area of the base?

_____

b. What is the volume of the prism?

_____

3. The rectangular prism below has a volume of 126 cubic centimeters.

Area of base = 42 cm²

What is the height of the prism?

_____

4. Solve.

a. I am a geometric solid with six faces. All of my faces are rectangular, but none is square. What shape am I?

_____

b. My 4 faces are triangular. What shape am I?

_____

5. Circle the rectangular prism below that has the greatest volume.

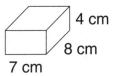

4 cm
8 cm
7 cm

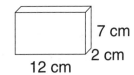

7 cm
2 cm
12 cm

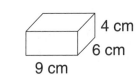

4 cm
6 cm
9 cm

Math Message: Number-Line Models

Use the above number line to help you answer Questions 1–10:

1. What is $\frac{1}{2}$ of 3? _____
2. What is $\frac{1}{4}$ of 2? _____
3. What is $\frac{3}{4}$ of 2? _____
4. What is $\frac{1}{3}$ of 3? _____
5. What is $\frac{1}{2}$ of $\frac{1}{2}$? _____
6. What is $\frac{1}{2}$ of $\frac{1}{4}$? _____
7. What is $\frac{1}{2}$ of $\frac{3}{4}$? _____
8. What is $\frac{1}{4}$ of $\frac{1}{2}$? _____
9. What is $\frac{1}{4}$ of $\frac{1}{4}$? _____
10. What is $\frac{1}{2}$ of $\frac{3}{8}$? _____

11. Explain how you figured out the answer to Question 10.

_____

_____

_____

_____

All (Winged) Creatures: Great and Small
The smallest bird is the bee hummingbird. It weighs about 2 grams (0.07 ounces) and is about 5.5 centimeters (2.2 inches) long. The largest bird is the ostrich. An adult ostrich can weigh more than 150 kilograms (330 pounds) and stand 2.5 meters (8 feet) tall. (It's no wonder that ostriches can't fly!) It would take more than 75,000 bee hummingbirds to balance one ostrich (if you could find a scale big enough).

Source: Britannica Online.

Paper-Folding Results

Record your work for the four problems you did in class. Sketch the folds and shading. Write an X on the parts that represent the answer.

1. $\frac{1}{2}$ of $\frac{1}{2}$ is _____.

2. $\frac{2}{3}$ of $\frac{1}{2}$ is _____.

3. $\frac{1}{4}$ of $\frac{2}{3}$ is _____.

4. $\frac{3}{4}$ of $\frac{1}{2}$ is _____.

Math Boxes 114

---

1. **a.** Write a 9-digit numeral that has a 4 in the hundred-thousands place, a 6 in the millions place, a 5 in the tens place, a 2 in the hundredths place, a 9 in the thousands place, and 3s in all of the other places.

_____

   b. Write this numeral in words.

_____

_____

---

2. Write a number model, and then solve the problem.

Of the 32 ice-cream cones served at Pearl's Ice Cream shop today, $\frac{3}{4}$ were chocolate. How many chocolate ice-cream cones were served?

Number Model: _____   Answer: _____

---

3. Add or subtract.

  a.   703.03   **b.**   243.84   **c.**   438.29   **d.**   278.6
       − 655.4   + 176.56   + 105.003   − 89.45

---

4. Write an algebraic expression for each of the following statements. The first one is done for you.

  a. Maria is *y* years old. Sheila is 10 years older than Maria. How old is Sheila?   *10 + y*

  b. Franklin has *c* miniature cars. Rosie has 4 more cars than twice as many as Franklin has. How many cars does Rosie have?   _____

  c. Lucinda goes to sleep-away camp for *D* days each summer. Rhonda goes to camp for 1 less day than half of Lucinda's number of days. For how many days does Rhonda go to camp?   _____

  d. Cheryl read *B* books this year. Ralph read 3 more than 5 times as many books as Cheryl. How many books did Ralph read?   _____

Math Message: Fraction Multiplication

1. Use the rectangle at the right to sketch how you would fold paper to help you find $\frac{1}{3}$ of $\frac{2}{3}$.

   What is $\frac{1}{3}$ of $\frac{2}{3}$? _____

2. Use the rectangle at the right to sketch how you would fold paper to help you find $\frac{1}{4}$ of $\frac{3}{5}$.

   What is $\frac{1}{4}$ of $\frac{3}{5}$? _____

3. Rewrite "$\frac{2}{3}$ of $\frac{3}{4}$" using the multiplication symbol ($*$). _____

4. Rewrite the following using the multiplication symbol ($*$).

   a. $\frac{1}{4}$ of $\frac{1}{3}$ _____

   b. $\frac{4}{5}$ of $\frac{2}{3}$ _____

   c. $\frac{1}{6}$ of $\frac{1}{4}$ _____

   d. $\frac{3}{7}$ of $\frac{2}{5}$ _____

An Area Model for Fraction Multiplication

Use the rectangle at the right to find $\frac{2}{3} * \frac{3}{4}$.

$\frac{2}{3} * \frac{3}{4} =$ _____

Your completed drawing is called an **area model.**

Use area models to complete the following.

1.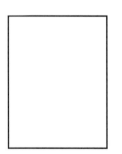

$\frac{2}{3} * \frac{1}{5} =$ _____

2.

$\frac{3}{4} * \frac{2}{5} =$ _____

3.

$\frac{1}{4} * \frac{5}{6} =$ _____

4.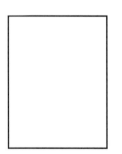

$\frac{3}{8} * \frac{3}{5} =$ _____

5.

$\frac{1}{2} * \frac{5}{8} =$ _____

6.

$\frac{5}{6} * \frac{4}{5} =$ _____

7. Make up your own fraction multiplication problem.
Use an area model to help you solve it.

_____

            Use with Lesson 115.

An Algorithm for Fraction Multiplication

1. Look carefully at the fractions on journal page 462. What is the relationship between the numerators and the denominators of the two fractions being multiplied and the numerator and denominator of their product?

   _____

   _____

   _____

   _____

2. Describe a way to multiply two fractions.

   _____

   _____

   _____

   _____

3. Multiply the following fractions, using the shortcut discussed in class.

   a. $\frac{1}{3} * \frac{1}{5} =$ _____

   b. $\frac{2}{3} * \frac{1}{3} =$ _____

   c. $\frac{3}{10} * \frac{7}{10} =$ _____

   d. $\frac{5}{8} * \frac{1}{4} =$ _____

   e. $\frac{3}{8} * \frac{5}{6} =$ _____

   f. $\frac{2}{5} * \frac{5}{12} =$ _____

   g. $\frac{4}{5} * \frac{2}{5} =$ _____

   h. $\frac{4}{9} * \frac{3}{7} =$ _____

Did You Know?

Cashing In on Fractions

Torn money might be worth something. If you have $\frac{3}{5}$ or more of a bill, it can be redeemed for its full face value. If you have less than $\frac{3}{5}$ but more than $\frac{2}{5}$ of a bill, it can be redeemed for $\frac{1}{2}$ of its face value. If you have $\frac{2}{5}$ or less, your bill is worthless.

Source: *You Can't Count a Billion Dollars.*

Math Boxes 115

1. Draw a figure with a perimeter of 24 units and an area of 20 square units.

1 unit 1 square unit

2. Complete the "What's My Rule?" table and state the rule.

Rule

X	Y
$\frac{1}{3}$	
	0
$\frac{5}{3}$	4
	2
-2	$\frac{1}{3}$

3. Add or subtract.

a. _____ $= \frac{28}{9} - 2\frac{2}{7}$

b. _____ $= 5\frac{4}{5} - 3\frac{7}{4}$

c. _____ $= 3\frac{1}{8} + 16/6$

d. _____ $= 2\frac{4}{9} + 3\frac{7}{3}$

e. _____ $= 1\frac{9}{10} - \frac{15}{8}$

4. a. Triangles *A* and *B* are partially covered. One of them has an obtuse angle. Which triangle could this be? (Circle *A* or *B*.)

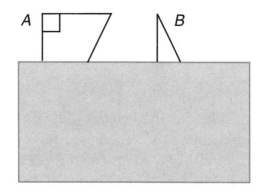

b. Draw what the triangles might look like if the drawings were complete.

Math Message: A Blast from the Past

1. From *Kindergarten Everyday Mathematics:*

   This slice of pizza is what
   fraction of the whole pizza? _____

2. From *First Grade Everyday Mathematics:*

   Write a fraction in each part of the diagrams below. Then color the figures as directed.

   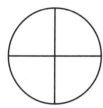 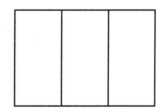 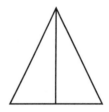

   a. Color $\frac{3}{4}$.   **b.** Color $\frac{2}{3}$.   **c.** Color $\frac{2}{2}$.

3. From *Second Grade Everyday Mathematics:*

   a. Color $\frac{1}{4}$ of the beads.   **b.** Color $\frac{1}{8}$ of the beads.

   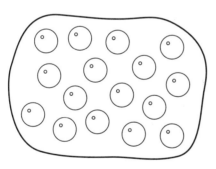 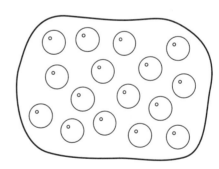

4. From *Third Grade Everyday Mathematics:*

   a. $\frac{1}{2}$ of $\frac{1}{4}$ = _____   **b.** $\frac{1}{8}$ of $\frac{1}{2}$ = _____   **c.** $\frac{1}{2}$ of $\frac{1}{8}$ = _____

5. From *Fourth Grade Everyday Mathematics:*

   Cross out $\frac{5}{6}$ of the dimes.

Area Models

Draw an area model for each product. Then write the product as a fraction or as a mixed number.

Example: $\frac{2}{3} * 2 = $ ___$\frac{4}{3}$ or $1\frac{1}{3}$___

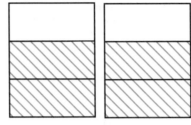

1. $\frac{1}{3} * 4 = $ _____

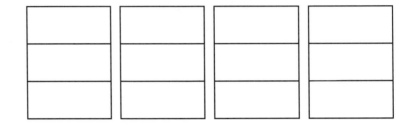

2. $\frac{1}{4} * 3 = $ _____

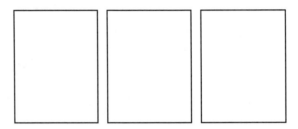

3. $2 * \frac{3}{5} = $ _____

4. $\frac{3}{8} * 3 = $ _____

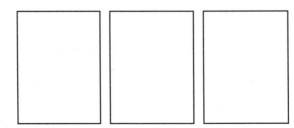

Use with Lesson 116.

Using the Fraction Multiplication Algorithm

> **An Algorithm for Fraction Multiplication**
>
> $$\frac{a}{b} * \frac{c}{d} = \frac{a * c}{b * d}$$
>
> The denominator of the product is the product of the denominators, and the numerator of the product is the product of the numerators.

Example: $\frac{2}{3} * 2$

$\frac{2}{3} * 2 = \frac{2}{3} * \frac{2}{1}$ Think of 2 as $\frac{2}{1}$.

$\quad\quad = \frac{2 * 2}{3 * 1}$ Apply the algorithm.

$\quad\quad = \frac{4}{3}$ or $1\frac{1}{3}$ Calculate the numerator and denominator.

Use the fraction multiplication algorithm to calculate the following products:

1. $\frac{3}{4} * 6 =$ _____   **2.** $\frac{7}{8} * 3 =$ _____

3. $\frac{3}{10} * 5 =$ _____   **4.** $6 * \frac{4}{5} =$ _____

5. $\frac{5}{3} * 9 =$ _____   **6.** $\frac{3}{8} * 12 =$ _____

7. $\frac{1}{8} * 5 =$ _____   **8.** $20 * \frac{3}{4} =$ _____

9. $\frac{5}{6} * 14 =$ _____   **10.** $27 * \frac{2}{9} =$ _____

Did You Know

Tree Fractions

On some trees, the leaves grow at a constant angle to each other. For example, the leaves on an elm tree are separated by angles of about 180°, or $\frac{1}{2}$ of 360°. Beech tree leaves are separated by angles of $\frac{1}{3}$ of 360°; oak and cherry leaves by angles of $\frac{2}{5}$ of 360°; pear leaves by angles of $\frac{3}{8}$ of 360°; and willow leaves by angles of $\frac{5}{13}$ of 360°.

Do you notice any pattern in these fractions? (*Hint:* Recall the Fibonacci sequence of numbers— 1, 1, 2, 3, 5, 8, 13, ...)

Source: *Metamorphosis.*

Math Boxes 116

---

1. Insert parentheses to make each expression true.

   a. $-28 + 43 * 2 = 30$

   b. $-19 = 12 / 2 * 6 + (-20)$

   c. $16 = 12 / 2 * 6 + (-20)$

   d. $24 / 6 - (-2) + 5 = 8$

   e. $24 / 6 - (-2) + 5 = 11$

2. Solve.

                                              Solution:

   a. $\frac{5}{9} = \frac{x}{18}$ _____

   b. $\frac{8}{25} = \frac{40}{y}$ _____

   c. $6/14 = \frac{w}{49}$ _____

   d. $\frac{28}{z} = \frac{7}{9}$ _____

   e. $\frac{44}{77} = \frac{4}{v}$ _____

---

3. **a.** Mark and label -1.7, 0.8, -1.3, and 1.9 on the number line.

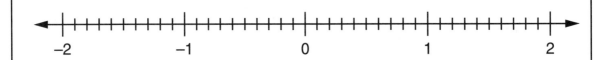

   b. What number is 1 less than -1.7? _____

   c. What number is 1 more than 1.9? _____

---

4. Measure angle Q to the nearest degree.

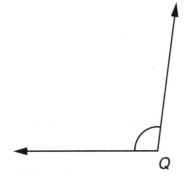

Measure of angle Q is

about _____°.

5. Complete the table.

Fraction	Decimal	Percent
$\frac{7}{8}$		
	0.89	
		70%
	0.125	
$\frac{7}{50}$		

Math Message

Review Converting Fractions to Mixed Numbers

You know that fractions larger than 1 can be written in several ways.

Whole
hexagon

Example:

If a 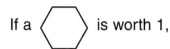 is worth 1,

what is  worth?

The mixed-number name is $3\frac{5}{6}$ ($3\frac{5}{6}$ means $3 + \frac{5}{6}$).

The fraction name is $\frac{23}{6}$. Think sixths:

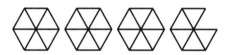

$3\frac{5}{6}$, $3 + \frac{5}{6}$, and $\frac{23}{6}$ are different names for the same number.

1. Write the following mixed numbers as fractions.

   a. $2\frac{3}{5}$ = _____   b. $4\frac{7}{8}$ = _____

   c. $1\frac{2}{3}$ = _____   d. $3\frac{6}{4}$ = _____

2. Write the following fractions as mixed or whole numbers.

   a. $\frac{7}{3}$ = _____   b. $\frac{6}{1}$ = _____

   c. $\frac{18}{4}$ = _____   d. $\frac{9}{3}$ = _____

3. Add.

   a. $2 + \frac{7}{8}$ = _____   b. $1 + \frac{3}{4}$ = _____

   c. $3 + \frac{3}{5}$ = _____   d. $6 + 2\frac{1}{3}$ = _____

Multiplication of Fractions and Mixed Numbers

Example 1: **Use partial products.**

$2\frac{1}{3} * 2\frac{1}{2} = (2 + \frac{1}{3}) * (2 + \frac{1}{2})$	$3\frac{1}{4} * \frac{2}{5} = (3 + \frac{1}{4}) * \frac{2}{5}$
$2 * 2 = \quad 4$	$3 * \frac{2}{5} = \frac{6}{5} = \quad 1\frac{1}{5}$
$2 * \frac{1}{2} = \quad 1$	$\frac{1}{4} * \frac{2}{5} = \frac{2}{20} = \quad + \frac{1}{10}$
$\frac{1}{3} * 2 = \quad \frac{2}{3}$	$\overline{\qquad\qquad 1\frac{3}{10}}$
$\frac{1}{3} * \frac{1}{2} = \quad + \frac{1}{6}$	
$\overline{\qquad 5\frac{5}{6}}$	

Example 2: **Convert mixed numbers to fractions.**

$2\frac{1}{3} * 2\frac{1}{2} = \frac{7}{3} * \frac{5}{2}$	$3\frac{1}{4} * \frac{2}{5} = \frac{13}{4} * \frac{2}{5}$
$= \frac{35}{6} = 5\frac{5}{6}$	$= \frac{26}{20} = 1\frac{6}{20} = 1\frac{3}{10}$

Solve the following fraction and mixed-number multiplication problems.

1. $3\frac{1}{2} * 2\frac{1}{5} =$ _____

2. $10\frac{3}{4} * \frac{1}{2} =$ _____

3. The surface of a calculator is approximately a rectangular prism. The back face has an area of about

_____ in².

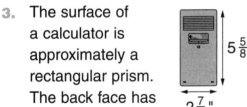

4. The area of a sheet of notebook paper is about

_____ in².

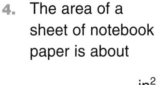

5. The area of a computer disk is about

_____ in².

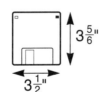

6. The area of the flag is about

_____ yd².

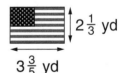

7. Is the area of the flag greater or less than the area of your desk or tabletop? _____

Track Records on the Moon and the Planets

Every moon and planet in our solar system pulls objects toward it with the force called **gravity.**

In the 1992 Olympics, the winning high jump was 7 feet 8 inches, or $7\frac{2}{3}$ feet. The winning pole vault was 19 feet. Suppose that the Olympics were held on Earth's Moon, or on Jupiter, Mars, or Venus. What height might we expect for a winning high jump, or a winning pole vault?

1. On the Moon, one could jump about 6 times as high as on Earth. What would be the height of the winning

    high jump? About _____ feet. Pole vault? about _____ feet

2. On Jupiter, one could jump about $\frac{3}{8}$ as high as on Earth. What would be the height of the winning

    high jump? About _____ feet.   Pole vault? about _____ feet

3. On Mars, one could jump about $2\frac{2}{3}$ times as high as on Earth. What would be the height of the winning

    high jump? About _____ feet. Pole vault? about _____ feet

4. On Venus, one could jump about $1\frac{1}{7}$ times as high as on Earth. What would be the height of the winning

    high jump? About _____ feet. Pole vault? about _____ feet

5. Is Jupiter's pull of gravity stronger or weaker than Earth's? Explain your reasoning.

    _____

    _____

    _____

Challenge

6. The winning pole-vault height given above was rounded to the nearest whole number. The actual winning height was 19 feet $\frac{1}{4}$ inch. If you used this actual measurement, about how high would the winning jump be

    on the Moon? _____   on Jupiter? _____

    on Mars? _____   on Venus? _____

Math Boxes 117

---

1. **a.** Write a 7-digit numeral that has 5 in the ten-thousands place, 6 in the tenths place, 9 in the ones place, 7 in the hundreds place, 3 in the hundredths place, and 2s in all of the other places.

_____

b. Write this numeral in words.

_____

_____

---

2. Write a number model, and then solve the problem.

Five out of 6 shoes in Norma's closet are blue. She has 40 blue shoes. How many shoes are in Norma's closet?

Number Model: _____   Answer: _____

---

3. Add or subtract.

a. 385.02 + 7.99 = _____

b. 61.43 + 29.7 = _____

c. _____ = 496.12 − 224.87

d. _____ = 300.43 − 265.7

e. _____ = 918.3 − 69.25

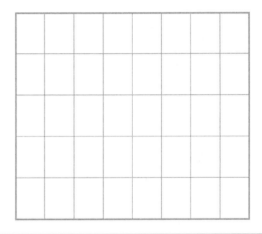

---

4. Write an algebraic expression for each of the following statements:

a. Jim rode m miles on his bicycle. Alva rode 3 times as many miles. How far did Alva ride? _____

b. Bob swam for S minutes. Steven swam for $\frac{1}{2}$ hour more than 3 times as many minutes as Bob. How long did Steven swim? _____

c. Curt's pet mouse had P babies. Karen's pet mouse had 6 fewer babies. How many babies did Karen's mouse have? _____

Finding a Percent of a Number

1. The Madison Middle School boys' basketball team has played five games. The table at the right shows the number of shots taken by each player, and the percent of shots that were baskets. Study the example. Then calculate the number of baskets made by each player.

   Example: Bill took 15 shots. He made a basket on 40% of these shots.

   $40\% = \frac{40}{100}$ or $\frac{4}{10}$

   $\frac{4}{10}$ of $15 = \frac{4}{10} * \frac{15}{1} =$

   $\frac{4 * 15}{10 * 1} = \frac{60}{10} = 6$

   Bill made 6 baskets.

Player	Shots Taken	Percent Made	Baskets
Bill	15	40%	*6*
Amit	40	30%	
Josh	25	60%	
Kevin	8	75%	
Mike	60	25%	
Zheng	44	25%	
Andre	50	10%	
David	25	20%	
Bob	18	50%	
Lars	15	20%	
Justin	28	25%	

2. On the basis of shooting ability, which five players might you select as the starting lineup for the next basketball game?

   _____

3. What other factors might you consider when making this decision?

   _____

   _____

4. Which player(s) might you encourage to shoot more often?

   _____ Why? _____

   _____

5. Which player(s) would you encourage to pass more often?

   _____ Why? _____

   _____

Calculating a Discount

Example: The list price for a toaster is $45. The toaster is sold at a 12% discount (12% off the list price). What is the savings? (*Reminder:* 12% = $\frac{12}{100}$ = 0.12)

Paper and pencil:

$$12\% \text{ of } \$45 = \frac{12}{100} * 45 = \frac{12}{100} * \frac{45}{1}$$

$$= \frac{12 * 45}{100 * 1} = \frac{540}{100}$$

$$= \$5.40$$

Calculator:

Enter 0.12 [×] 45 [=]; interpret answer 5.4 as $5.40.

First use your percent sense to estimate the discount for each item in the table below. The **discount** is the amount by which the list price of an item is reduced. It is the amount the customer saves.

Then use your calculator or paper and pencil to calculate the discount.
(If necessary, round to the nearest cent.)

Item	List Price	Percent of Discount	Estimated Discount	Calculated Discount
Clock radio	$33.00	20%		
Calculator	$60.00	7%		
Sweater	$20.00	42%		
Tent	$180.00	30%		
Bicycle	$200.00	17%		
Computer	$980.00	25%		
Skis	$325.00	28%		
Double CD	$29.99	15%		
Jacket	$110.00	55%		

Math Boxes 118

1. Draw a figure with a perimeter of 36 units and an area of 80 square units.

1 <u>unit</u>   1 square unit

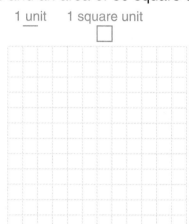

2. Complete the "What's My Rule?" table and state the rule.

Rule	d	m
	2	
	3	1
	6	2
		$\frac{1}{3}$
	10	

3. Add or subtract.

a. $\quad \frac{3}{8}$
$\quad +\frac{5}{9}$
$\quad \overline{}$

b. $\quad \frac{29}{4}$
$\quad +1\frac{2}{5}$
$\quad \overline{}$

c. $\quad \frac{18}{7}$
$\quad -2\frac{1}{5}$
$\quad \overline{}$

d. $\quad 4\frac{2}{3}$
$\quad -3\frac{7}{8}$
$\quad \overline{}$

e. $\quad 2\frac{14}{10}$
$\quad +1\frac{8}{9}$
$\quad \overline{}$

f. $\quad 8\frac{20}{7}$
$\quad -6\frac{3}{9}$
$\quad \overline{}$

4. Measure each angle. Then circle the acute angle.

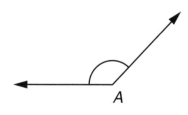
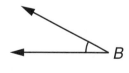
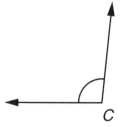

a. The measure of $\angle A$ is about _____°.

b. The measure of $\angle B$ is about _____°.

c. The measure of $\angle C$ is about _____°.

Math Message: Unit Fractions and Unit Percents

1. If 12 counters are $\frac{1}{5}$ of a set, how many counters are in the set?

   _____ counters

2. If 15 counters are $\frac{1}{7}$ of a set, how many counters are in the set?

   _____ counters

3. If 31 pages are $\frac{1}{8}$ of a book, how many pages are in the book?

   _____ pages

4. If 13 marbles are 1% of the marbles in a jar, how many marbles are in the jar?

   _____ marbles

5. If $5.43 is 1% of the cost of a TV, what does the TV cost?

   _____ dollars

6. If 84 counters are 10% of a set, how many counters are in the set?

   _____ counters

7. After 1 hour and 40 minutes, Dorothy had read 120 pages of a 300-page book. If she continues reading at the same rate, about how long will it take her to read the entire book?

   _____ minutes

8. In its most recent game, the Lincoln Junior High basketball team made 36 baskets, which was 48% of the shots team members tried. How many shots did they try?

   _____ shots

9. Eighty-four persons attended the school concert. This was 70% of the number expected to attend. How many persons were expected to attend?

   _____ people

Using a Unit Fraction to Find the Whole

Example 1:   Alex collects sports cards. Seventy of his cards feature
             basketball players. These 70 cards are $\frac{2}{3}$ of Alex's collection.
             How many sports cards does Alex have?

             $\frac{2}{3}$ is worth 70 cards. So $\frac{1}{3}$ is worth 35 cards.

             Therefore, Alex has 3 * 35, or 105 cards.

Example 2:   Barb's mother baked cookies. She gave Barb 24 cookies, which
             was $\frac{3}{5}$ of the total she baked. How many cookies did she bake?

             $\frac{3}{5}$ is worth 24 cookies. So $\frac{1}{5}$ is worth 8 cookies.

             Barb's mother baked 5 * 8, or 40 cookies.

1. Six jars are filled with cookies. The number of cookies in each jar is not
   known. For each clue given below, find the number of cookies in the jar.

Clue	Number of Cookies in Jar
a. $\frac{1}{2}$ jar contains 31 cookies.	
b. $\frac{2}{8}$ jar contains 10 cookies.	
c. $\frac{3}{5}$ jar contains 36 cookies.	
d. $\frac{3}{8}$ jar contains 21 cookies.	
e. $\frac{4}{7}$ jar contains 64 cookies.	
f. $\frac{3}{11}$ jar contains 45 cookies.	

2. Alan is walking to a friend's house. He covered $\frac{6}{10}$
   of the distance in 48 minutes. If he continues at the
   same speed, about how long will the entire
   walk take?   _____

3. A candle burned $\frac{3}{8}$ of the way down in 36 minutes. If it
   continues to burn at the same rate, about how many
   more minutes will the candle burn before it is used up?   _____

Using a Unit Percent to Find the Whole

Example 1: The sale price of a CD player is $120. It is on sale for 60% of its list price. What is the list price?

60% is worth $120.

So 1% is worth $2 ($\frac{120}{60} = 2$),

and 100% is worth $200 (100 $*$ 2 = 200).

The list price is $200.

Example 2: A toaster is on sale for 80% of its list price. The sale price is $40. What is the list price?

80% is worth $40.

So 1% is worth $0.50 ($\frac{40}{80} = 0.5$),

and 100% is worth $50 (100 $*$ 0.5 = 50).

The list price is $50.

1. Use your percent sense to estimate the list price for each item. Then calculate the list price. (*Hint:* First use your calculator to find what 1% is worth.)

Sale Price	Percent of List Price	Estimated List Price	Calculated List Price
$120.00	60%	$180	$200
$100.00	50%		
$8.00	32%		
$255.00	85%		
$77.00	55%		
$80.00	40%		
$9.00	60%		
$112.50	75%		
$450.00	90%		

Math Boxes 119

1. Insert parentheses to make each expression true.

a. $-14 + 36 / 4 - (-2) = -3$

b. $-14 + 36 / 4 - (-2) = -8$

c. $15 = (-20) - (-5) + 10 * 3$

d. $-35 = (-20) - (-5) + 10 * 3$

e. $8 * 6 - (-24) + 71 = 311$

2. Solve.

Solution

a. $m/10 = \frac{45}{50}$ _____

b. $\frac{56}{64} = \frac{7}{n}$ _____

c. $\frac{k}{48} = \frac{3}{8}$ _____

d. $\frac{4}{30} = \frac{12}{p}$ _____

e. $\frac{2}{18} = \frac{q}{180}$ _____

3. Name the number for each point marked on the number line.

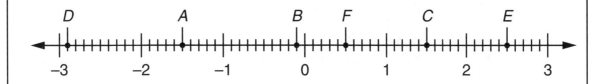

$A =$ _____ $B =$ _____ $C =$ _____

$D =$ _____ $E =$ _____ $F =$ _____

4. Measure angle S to the nearest degree.

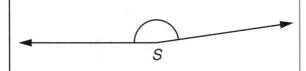

The measure of $\angle S$ is about _____ °.

5. Complete the table.

Fraction	Decimal	Percent
$\frac{3}{20}$		
		9%
	0.6	
$\frac{7}{25}$		
		$33\frac{1}{3}\%$

My Heart Rate

The heart is an organ in your body that pumps blood through your blood vessels. The **heart rate** is the rate at which your heart pumps the blood. It is usually given as the number of **heartbeats per minute.** With each heartbeat, the arteries stretch and then go back to their normal size. This throbbing of the arteries is called the **pulse.** It is possible to feel a person's pulse. The **pulse rate** is the same as the heart rate.

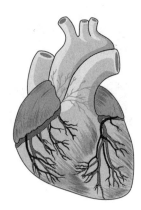

You can feel your pulse along your wrist, near the bone, below the thumb. You can also feel it in your neck: Run your index and middle fingers from your ear, past the curve of your jaw, and press them into the soft part of your neck just below your jaw.

Practice taking your own pulse for 15 seconds. Your partner can use the classroom clock or a watch to time you. Do this several times, until you are sure your count is accurate.

1. About how many times does your heart beat in 15 seconds? _____

2. At this rate, about how many times would it beat in 1 minute? _____

   In 1 hour? _____

   In 1 day? _____

   In 1 year? _____

3. Your fist and your heart are about the same size. Measure your fist with your ruler. Record the results.

   My heart is about _____ inches

   wide and _____ inches long.

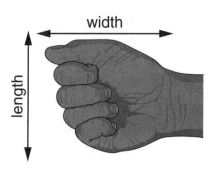

4. The heart weighs about 1 ounce per 12 pounds of body weight.

   Does your heart weigh more or less than 15 ounces? _____

480

Spoon Scramble

Materials   ☐ 3 spoons   ☐ deck of 16 *Spoon Scramble* cards

Number of players 4

Object of the game To be the first player in each round to get 4 cards of equal value, and to avoid getting all the letters in the word SPOONS.

Directions

1. Place the spoons in the center of the table.

2. Pick a player to be the dealer. The dealer shuffles and deals the cards facedown (4 to each player).

3. Players look at their cards. If any player has 4 cards of equal value, proceed to Step 6 below. Otherwise, each player chooses 1 card to discard.

Example: Blair has these cards: $\frac{1}{4}$ of 24; $3\frac{1}{2} * 2$; 50% of 12; 0.10 * 90. The object is to get 4 cards of equal value. She should discard either $3\frac{1}{2} * 2$ or 0.10 * 90.

4. Players pass their discarded cards facedown to the player on the left.

5. Each player picks up the new card and chooses a card to discard. The passing of the cards should proceed as quickly as possible.

6. As soon as a player has 4 cards of equal value, that player places the cards faceup on the table and grabs a spoon.

7. As soon as the other players see this happen, they grab for the remaining spoons.

8. The player left without a spoon in each round is assigned a letter from the word SPOONS, starting with the first letter. If a player incorrectly claims to have 4 cards of equal value, that player—instead of the player left without a spoon—receives a letter from the word.

9. Players put the spoons back in the center of the table. The dealer shuffles and deals the cards. A new round begins (as in Step 3 above).

10. Play continues until three players get all the letters in the word SPOONS. The player who does not have all the letters is the winner.

Variations

- For 3 players: Eliminate one set of 4 equivalent *Spoon Scramble* cards and one spoon.

- Players can make their own deck of *Spoon Scramble* cards. Each player writes four computation problems with equivalent answers on four index cards. Check to be sure that different players have chosen different values.

Math Boxes 120

1. The area of the cover of the dictionary is about

_____ .

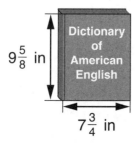

$9\frac{5}{8}$ in

Dictionary of American English

$7\frac{3}{4}$ in

2. Marlene randomly chose 25 cards from a deck. Forty percent of these cards were hearts. How many hearts did she draw?

_____

3. Write a number model to describe each of the shaded rectangles below.

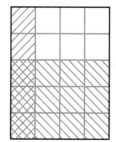

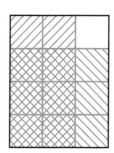

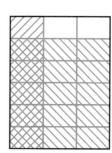

a. _____ b. _____ c. _____

4. Janet wants a pair of in-line skates. The list price is $63. The skates are on sale at 30% off. How much will Janet have to pay for the skates?

_____

Explain how you solved the problem.

_____

_____

_____

5. Solve.

Solution

a. $\frac{3}{2} * y = \frac{9}{10}$ _____

b. $m * \frac{4}{5} = \frac{12}{40}$ _____

c. $1\frac{3}{4} * s = \frac{7}{32}$ _____

d. $\frac{9}{10} * t = \frac{45}{40}$ _____

e. $\frac{25}{32} = k * \frac{5}{8}$ _____

Math Message: Rates

1. Complete each table using the given information. Then answer the question below each table.

   a. It would take 27,000 spiders, each spinning a single web, to produce a pound of spider web.

Number of Spiders	27,000	54,000			
Pounds of Spider Web	1	2	3	4	5

   At this rate, how many spiders, each spinning a single web, would be needed to produce 10 pounds of spider web?

   _____ spiders

   b. The deer botfly flies so fast that it is almost invisible to the human eye. In 1 minute it can travel 13 miles.

Miles	13				
Minutes	1	2	3	4	5

   At this rate, how far could a deer botfly travel in 1 hour? _____ miles

2. Solve the following rate problems. Make a table if it will help you.

   a. About 50 gallons of maple sap are needed to make 1 gallon of maple syrup. How many gallons of maple sap are needed to make 20 gallons of maple syrup?

   about _____ gallons

   b. For 186 days a year, the Sun is not visible at the North Pole. During a 5-year period, for about how many days is the Sun not visible?

   about _____ days

   c. In a beehive, about $1\frac{1}{2}$ ounces of beeswax are used to build a honeycomb that holds 4 pounds of honey. How much beeswax is needed to build a honeycomb that could hold 20 pounds of honey?

   about _____ ounces

Source: *2201 Fascinating Facts.*

Exercise and Your Heart

Exercise increases the rate at which a person's heart beats.
Very strenuous exercise can double the heart rate.

Work with a partner to find out how exercise affects your heart rate.

1. Sit quietly for a minute. Then have your partner time you for 15 seconds
    while you take your pulse. Record the number of heartbeats in the first row
    of the table below.

2. Step up on and down from a chair 5 times without stopping. As soon as
    you finish, take your pulse for 15 seconds while your partner times you.
    Record the number of heartbeats in the second row of the table.

3. Sit quietly. While you are resting, your partner can do 5 step-ups, and you
    can time your partner.

4. When your pulse is almost back to normal, step up on and down from the
    chair 10 times. Record the number of heartbeats in 15 seconds in the third
    row of the table. Then rest while your partner does 10 step-ups.

5. Repeat for 15, 20, and 25 step-ups.

6. Why is it important that all students
    step up at the same rate?

    _____

    _____

    _____

    _____

Step-ups	Heartbeats per 15 Seconds
0	
5	
10	
15	
20	
25	

Have a Heart
Giraffes do! Their hearts weigh up to 25 pounds and are up to
2 feet across. A giraffe's heart has to work hard to move blood
up that neck, which can be 10 to 12 feet long. The average
giraffe's blood pressure is three times that of a human.

Source: *Beyond Belief!!*

My Heart-Rate Profile

1. Make a line graph of the data in your table on journal page 484.

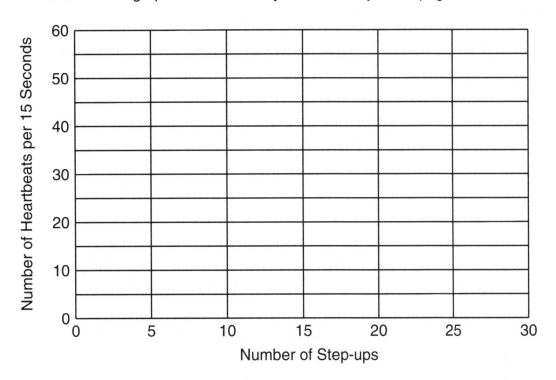

2. Make a prediction: What will your heart rate be if you do 30 step-ups?

   about _____ heartbeats in 15 seconds

3. When you exercise, you must be careful not to put too much stress on your heart. Exercise experts often recommend a "target" heart rate to reach during exercise. The target heart rate varies, depending on a person's age and health, but the following rule is sometimes used.

   Target heart rate during exercise:

   Subtract your age from 220. Multiply the result by 2. Then divide by 3.

   The result is the target number of heartbeats per minute.

   a. According to this rule, what is your target heart rate during exercise?

      about _____ heartbeats per minute

   b. That's about how many beats in 15 seconds?

      about _____ heartbeats

My Class's Heart-Rate Profile

1. Complete the table on the number of heartbeats per 15 seconds.

Number of Step-ups	Maximum	Minimum	Range	Median
0				
5				
10				
15				
20				
25				

2. Make a line graph of the medians on the grid on journal page 485. Use a colored pencil or crayon. Label this line "Class Profile." Label the other line "My Own Profile."

Extension

3. Look up your normal heart rate on journal page 484. Record it here. _____

Suppose that you exercised regularly and reduced your heart rate by 10 beats per minute.

How many heartbeats would you save per hour?

about _____ heartbeats

How many heartbeats would you save per day?

about _____ heartbeats

Blood for Miles
There are about 5 million red blood cells and between five and ten thousand white blood cells in 1 mL of blood from an average man. If all of one man's blood cells were lined up side by side, they would wrap around the Earth about seven times.
Source: *The Odd Book of Data.*

Use with Lesson 121.

Math Boxes 121

1. **a.** Make up a set of 15 numbers with the following landmarks:

    Maximum: 43

    Minimum: 16

    Median: 28

    Mode: 16

    _____

    _____

    _____

    b. Make a bar graph for the data.

2. Write five other names for $2\frac{3}{4}$.

    a. _____

    b. _____

    c. _____

    d. _____

    e. _____

3. Find the volume of the prism.

    Volume of a Triangular Prism
    Volume = Area of the base * height

    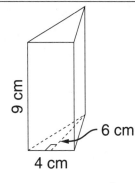

    Volume: _____ cm^3

4. A large box of candies costs $24.00. Patel paid $\frac{1}{8}$ of the total cost, Martha paid $\frac{1}{3}$, Kim paid $\frac{3}{12}$, Raye paid $\frac{1}{4}$, and Stewart paid the rest. How much did each person pay?

    Patel: _____

    Raye: _____

    Martha: _____

    Stewart: _____

    Kim: _____

Math Message: Review of Ratios

1. What is the ratio of the length of line segment
   AB to the length of line segment *CD*?   _____

2. Circle the pair of line segments whose lengths have the same ratio
   as $\overline{AB}$ to $\overline{CD}$ in Problem 1.

   (a)

   (b)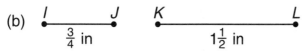

   (c)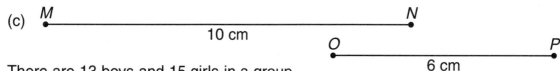

3. There are 13 boys and 15 girls in a group.
   What fractional part of the group is boys?   _____

4. Problem 3 was given to groups of 13-year-olds, 17-year-olds, and adults. The
   answers and the percent of each group that gave those particular answers are
   shown in the table below.

   a. What mistake was made by the people who gave the answer $\frac{15}{28}$?

   _____

   b. What mistake was made by the people who gave the answer $\frac{13}{15}$?

   _____

Answers	13-year-olds	17-year-olds	Adults
13/28	20%	36%	25%
$\frac{13}{28}$ written as a decimal	0%	0%	1%
$\frac{13}{15}$ or $0.8\overline{6}$	17%	17%	15%
$\frac{15}{18}$	2%	2%	3%
Other incorrect answers	44%	29%	35%
Don't know	12%	13%	21%
No answer	5%	2%	1%

The Heart Pump

Your heart is the strongest muscle in your body. It needs to be, because it never rests. Every day of your life, 24 hours a day, your heart pumps blood throughout your body. The blood carries the **nutrients** and **oxygen** your body needs to function.

You breathe oxygen into your lungs. The oxygen passes from your lungs into your bloodstream. As your heart pumps blood throughout your body, the oxygen is deposited in the cells of your body and is replaced by waste products, mainly **carbon dioxide.** The blood carries the carbon dioxide back to your lungs, which get rid of the carbon dioxide as you exhale. The carbon dioxide is replaced by oxygen, and the cycle begins again.

The amount of blood the heart pumps in 1 minute is called the **cardiac output.** To find your cardiac output, you need to know your **heart rate** and the average amount of blood your heart pumps with each heartbeat. Cardiac output is calculated as follows:

Cardiac output = amount of blood pumped per heartbeat $*$ heart rate

On average, the heart of a fifth grader pumps about 1.6 fluid ounces of blood with each heartbeat. If your heart beats about 90 times per minute, then your heart pumps about 1.6 $*$ 90, or 144, fluid ounces of blood per minute. Your cardiac output would be about 144 fluid ounces, or $1\frac{1}{8}$ gallons of blood per minute. That's about 65 gallons of blood per hour. Imagine having to do this much work, around the clock, every day of your life! Can you see why your heart needs to be very strong?

A person's normal heart rate decreases with age. A newborn's heart rate can be as high as 110 to 160 beats per minute. For 10-year-olds, it is around 90 beats per minute; and for adults, between 70 and 80 beats per minute. It is not unusual for older people's hearts to beat as few as 50 to 65 times per minute.

Because cardiac output depends on a person's heart rate, it is not the same at all times. The more often the heart beats in 1 minute, the more blood is pumped throughout the body.

The Heart Pump (continued)

Pretend that your heart has been pumping the same amount of blood all of your life so far—about 65 gallons of blood per hour.

1. At that rate, about how many gallons of
   blood would your heart pump per day?   about _____ gallons

   About how many gallons per year?   about _____ gallons

2. At that rate, about how many gallons
   would it have pumped from the time you
   were born to your last birthday?   about _____ gallons

   Both heart rate and cardiac output increase with exercise. Look up your
   heart rate *at rest* in Problem 2 on journal page 480 and find the number of
   heartbeats after 25 step-ups in the table on page 484. Record them below.

   Heart rate *at rest:* _____

   Heartbeats per 15 seconds after 25 step-ups: _____

3. If your heart pumps about 1.6 fluid ounces
   of blood per heartbeat, about how much blood
   does it pump in 1 minute when you are at rest?   about _____ fl oz

4. A gallon is equal to 128 fluid ounces. About how
   many gallons of blood does your heart pump in
   1 minute when you are at rest?   about _____ gallon(s)

5. At the rate of heartbeats after 25 step-ups,
   about how many times would your heart beat
   per minute?   about _____ beats

6. Use your answer in Problem 5 above to find
   about how many fluid ounces of blood your
   heart would pump in 1 minute after 25 step-ups. about _____ fl oz

   About how many gallons?   about _____ gallon(s)

Exercise helps your heart grow larger and stronger. The larger and stronger
your heart is, the more blood it can pump with each heartbeat. A stronger heart
needs fewer heartbeats to pump the same amount of blood. This puts less of a
strain on the heart.

Math Boxes 122

1. Multiply.

    a. $\frac{3}{8} * \frac{7}{9} =$ _____

    b. $\frac{5}{7} * \frac{6}{11} =$ _____

    c. $1\frac{3}{4} * 3\frac{2}{5} =$ _____

    d. $2\frac{7}{6} * 1\frac{4}{5} =$ _____

    e. $\frac{28}{4} * \frac{8}{6} =$ _____

2. Rachel bought a pair of shoes for $15.89 and 2 pairs of socks for $1.49 each. She paid with a $20.00 bill. How much change should she have gotten?

_____

3. Find the area of the triangle.

> Area of a Triangle $A = \frac{1}{2} * b * h$

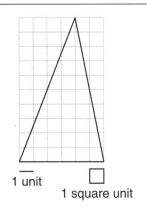

1 unit

☐ 1 square unit

Area: _____

4. Cherise lives on a chicken farm. Every morning she collects the eggs from the hen house. She collected 162 eggs on Monday, 104 eggs on Tuesday, and 157 eggs on Wednesday. She packed them into cartons, each containing 12 eggs. How many egg cartons can she fill completely?

_____

5. Mr. Kim's art class asked 50 people each to name their favorite kind of movie. The results are shown in the table. Complete the table and then make a circle graph of the results.

Kind of Movie	Number of People	Percent of Total
Action	23	
Comedy	14	
Romance	2	
Thriller	7	
Mystery	4	
Total		

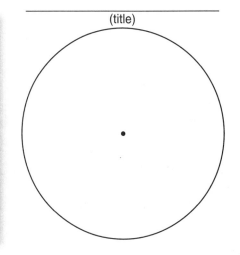

(title)

The Mathematics of Bicycle Pedaling

1. Your class will watch a videotape that shows people on different-sized bicycles riding between two marker poles. The poles were set exactly $\frac{1}{20}$ mile (264 feet) apart.

   For each rider, count the number of pedal turns the person makes to cover the distance between the poles. Do not use fractions; round down to the nearest whole number of turns. Then record the results in the second column in the table below.

   If your class does not use the videotape, your teacher will give you the pedal-turn data.

2. Wait for your teacher to give you directions for completing the rest of the table.

Bicycle	Pedal Turns (p) in 264 Feet	Diameter (d) of Wheel (inches)	Circumference (c) of Wheel (c = π * d) (feet)	Wheel Turns (w) in 264 Feet (264 / c)	Ratio of w to p (w/p)
1	19	27"	7.1'	37	1.9:1
2		26"	6.8'	39	
3		26"	6.8'		
4		24"			
5		24"			
6		20"	5.2'		
7		19"	5.0'		
8		15"			
9		22.5"	5.9'		

3. How many times will the wheels of Bicycle 1 turn in 1 mile? _____

   How many times will the pedals turn in 1 mile? _____

492

The Mathematics of Bicycle Pedaling (continued)

If you were very young when you first rode a bicycle, you probably rode a 1-speed bicycle. As you grew older, you may have ridden a multispeed bicycle. The most common bicycles sold today have 18 or 21 speeds. Many of the more expensive mountain bikes have 24 speeds.

A 1-speed bicycle has two discs with teeth, called the **pedal gear** and the **rear-wheel gear.** A chain loops over the pedal gear and over the rear-wheel gear.

A multispeed bicycle has more than one rear-wheel gear and usually more than one pedal gear. It also has one or two **shifters,** each connected to a gear by a **control cable.**

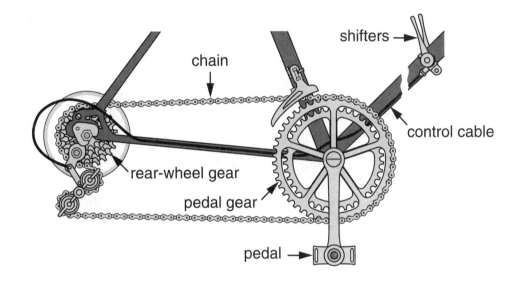

By moving a shifter, the rider makes the chain move from one gear to another. When the chain moves to a new gear, the bicycle becomes easier or harder to pedal, depending on the gears being used.

- When you shift gears to make the pedaling easy, the bicycle will not travel as far with each pedal turn as it did before shifting. You would use an "easy" gear when riding uphill or against a strong wind.

- When you shift gears to make the pedaling hard, the bicycle will travel farther with each pedal turn than it did before shifting. You would use a "hard" gear when riding on a flat stretch of road, downhill, or with a strong wind at your back.

The Mathematics of Bicycle Pedaling (continued)

In the investigation of bicycles, you have found that the ease of pedaling and the distance a bicycle travels as you pedal depend on the size of the wheels and on the ratio of the number of turns of the wheels to the number of turns of the pedals. Depending on the bicycle, this ratio can be as low as 0.8 to 1 and as high as 4.7 to 1.

- If the ratio is 1 wheel turn to 1 pedal turn, it means that the rear wheel turns exactly 1 time when the pedals make 1 turn.

- If the ratio is 0.8 to 1, it means that the rear wheel completes only 8/10 of a turn when the pedals make 1 turn. With a ratio of 0.8 to 1, pedaling would be very easy.

- If the ratio is 3 to 1, it means that the rear wheel makes 3 complete turns when the pedals make 1 turn. With a ratio of 3 to 1, pedaling would be quite hard, but you would travel a greater distance with one pedal turn.

Dedicated cyclists, however, are not concerned with the ratio of the number of wheel turns to the number of pedal turns. These cyclists discuss a special ratio called the **gear ratio**—the number of teeth on the rear-wheel gear to the number of teeth on the pedal gear. As you may have guessed, these two ratios are approximately the same. Counting gear teeth and finding the gear ratio is simply another way of finding how many wheel turns can be expected from a single turn of the pedals.

Sizing a Bicycle
Bicycle frames range in size from 19" to 25" in one-inch intervals. To decide on the right fit, a rider should stand in bare feet on a solid surface (not a carpet) and measure from the floor to the top of the leg (where the leg and hip meet). Subtract 13.75" from the measurement to get the correct frame size.

Source: *Sizes.*

Math Boxes 123

1. **a.** Make a stem-and-leaf plot for the data.

103, 94, 107, 99, 98, 110, 112,
120, 125, 100, 99, 102, 114,
114, 118, 99, 107, 99, 122, 114

Stems (10s)	Leaves (1s)

b. Find the data landmarks.

Maximum: _____

Minimum: _____

Median: _____

Mode: _____

---

2. Write five other names for $\frac{20}{5}$.

a. _____

b. _____

c. _____

d. _____

e. _____

---

3. Find the volume of the cylinder.

Volume of a Cylinder
Volume = Area of the base $*$ height

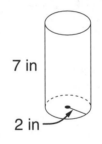

7 in

2 in

Volume: _____ in³

---

4. Martin missed $\frac{1}{8}$ of the 24 shots he took in a basketball game against the Rams.

a. What fraction of the shots did he make? _____

b. How many shots did he miss? _____

c. How many shots did he make? _____

d. What percent of his shots did he make? _____

American Tour: End-of-Year Projects

Work with a partner or in a small group on one or more of the following projects, or think up a project of your own. Each project has four steps.

1. **Plan and Do Research** Use the *American Tour Almanac* and other reference books to locate necessary and helpful data. Decide which information to use.

2. **Analyze Data** In order to complete the project, you will need to analyze and possibly transform the data you find in your sources.

3. **Record and Display Your Findings** Write a journal; make charts, graphs, tables, and other displays to record and show what you have found.

4. **Present Your Results** Report your findings to your classmates in clear and interesting ways.

Project 1: "Most" State, "Least" State, My State

Look up a variety of population and environmental statistics in the *American Tour Almanac* (pages 36–53) and in other sources. Create a display that shows which state has the most or the highest number, which has the least or lowest number, and the number for your state (if it is different). Then write a sentence or two for each comparison that describes how your state compares with the "most" and "least" states.

For example, if you live in Connecticut, you might make a comparison like the one below:

Population in 1990		
Most	California	29,760,021 people
Least	Wyoming	453,588 people
My State	Connecticut	3,287,116 people

My state's population is about $\frac{1}{9}$ the population of California, but about 7 times the population of Wyoming.

This is just one way you could make the comparison. There are many others. Find ways to make interesting and informative comparisons.

American Tour: End-of-Year Projects (continued)

Project 2: Then and Now

Pages 5–33 of the *American Tour Almanac* contain information about the United States during your lifetime and approximately 100 and 200 years ago. Use some of this information, as well as information from other sources, to create a series of bar graphs that compare the United States of your lifetime with the United States of approximately 100 and 200 years ago. For each graph, write a newspaper headline that describes an interesting pattern or fact shown by the graph.

For example, one of the bar graphs might compare the percent of the population living in urban areas in 1790, 1900, and 1990. It might look like the graph at the right.

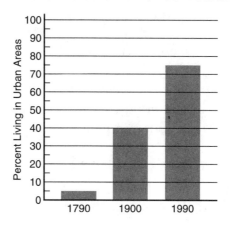

Percent of U.S. Population Living in Urban Areas Increases 15-Fold in 200 Years!

Some hints to keep in mind:

- Sometimes there will be no data for 200 years ago (1790). If this is the case, then compare 1890 or 1900 with the present.

- Sometimes there will be data for 1890 but not 1900, or no data for 1990 but estimated data for 2000. This is fine, as you are just trying to show change over approximately 100 years.

- The dates do not have to be the same for each bar graph. Just make sure to note on each graph which years you are comparing.

- Clearly label your graphs. Give them titles, and indicate which counts, measures, or percents you are comparing and the years for which you have data.

Project 3: State Almanac

Use the *American Tour Almanac* and other sources to create a State Almanac of interesting facts and features about your state (or another state). You might include the following information:

- the year your state became a state

- the number of 25- to 44-year-olds who might live in your state in 2020

- the number of times greater your state's population was in 1990 than in 1900

Illustrate the Almanac with graphs, pictures, and other displays that highlight unique features of your state.

Use with Lesson 124.

American Tour: End-of-Year Projects (continued)

Project 4: A Westward Journey

Use the information on pages 13 and 14 of the *American Tour Almanac* to help you write a journal that describes a trip across the country in 1840.

Begin the trip at a city on the east coast. From there, travel to St. Louis. Make part of this journey by foot, part by horseback, and part by stagecoach.

From St. Louis, take the trail of your choice west. Assume there is a road from St. Louis to Independence along the Missouri River.

Make approximately half of the journey from St. Louis to a city on the west coast by stagecoach and half by wagon train.

Find the number of days each part of the trip will take and the total traveling time from coast to coast.

You will need to make other decisions. How many hours per day could you travel by the various means of transportation? Do you need to rest along the way? Use your imagination.

For travel between cities in the northeast and St. Louis, you can use the highway map on page 54 as a rough guide to distances between cities. For other distances, use the map and scale on page 14.

You might, for example, begin as follows:

June 1	We departed Boston by stagecoach. Our destination was New York.
June 3	We arrived in New York. The journey from Boston took 2 days. The stagecoach traveled about 12 hours a day, covering around 100 miles each day. We were exhausted and so were the horses!
June 4	We left for Pittsburgh via Philadelphia and Lancaster, traveling by horseback.
June 12	The 400-mile horseback journey to Pittsburgh took 8 days. We covered about 65 miles per day, but we could not travel for two days due to driving rainstorms that washed out the road.

Project 5: Independent Research

Follow one of the "Explore More" suggestions on page 35 of the *American Tour Almanac,* or think up a project of your own.

Math Boxes 124

1. Multiply.

  a. $\frac{8}{11} * \frac{9}{10} =$ _____

  b. $1\frac{5}{6} * 3\frac{7}{8} =$ _____

  c. $2\frac{3}{4} * 2\frac{9}{5} =$ _____

  d. $\frac{24}{5} * \frac{7}{3} =$ _____

  e. $5\frac{1}{7} * 4\frac{1}{6} =$ _____

2. Jonah bought 3 tickets to a baseball game for $8.65 each. At the game, he bought a hot dog for $1.25 and a soft drink for $2.25. How much money did he spend in all?

_____

3. Find the area of the parallelogram.

Area of a Parallelogram $A = b * h$

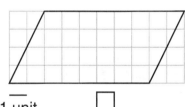

$\overline{}$
1 unit

□ 1 square unit

Area: _____ square units

4. To celebrate her birthday, Ms. Hahn decided to give each of the fifth graders one strand of her favorite kind of strawberry licorice whip. There are 179 fifth graders. The whips come 15 strands to a package at a cost of $1.19 per package.

  a. How many packages of licorice whips does Ms. Hahn need to buy?

_____

  b. How much will she spend?

_____

5. The table shows how Robert spent his allowance for the month of April. Complete the table and make a circle graph of the data.

Type of Expense	Amount Spent	Percent of Allowance
Snacks	$2.50	
Movie	$5.50	
Gum	$0.50	
Baseball Cards	$1.50	
Total		

(title)

Time to Reflect

1. During the past year, you studied many topics in mathematics—fractions, decimals, percents, estimation, number theory, algebra, geometry, area, volume, and so on. You used a variety of tools, including the calculator, Geometry Template, compass, and slide rule. You took part in the Million-Dollar Project, the American Tour, and other projects.

   a. What mathematics did you learn about this year that was new and interesting? Why did you find it interesting?

   _____

   _____

   _____

   b. What topics would you like to know more about?

   _____

2. Some mathematical skills are listed below. How would you rate yourself on each? Check the appropriate box. The last row is blank. Add another mathematical skill to the list, and rate yourself on it.

Skill	I know this well.	I am doing OK.	I need to do more work.
Knowing the multiplication and division facts			
Dividing whole numbers			
Working with fractions			
Estimating answers			
Using the Geometry Template			
Finding lengths, areas, and volumes			
Using a calculator			
Using the Probability Meter			

         Use with Lesson 125.

Math Boxes 125

---

1. The area of the stamp is about

_____.

$1\frac{7}{16}$ in [USA 32 Liberty stamp]

$1\frac{1}{2}$ in

2. Rita went to the batting cage with her father and took a turn at bat. The ball machine pitched the ball 40 times. She hit the ball 15% of the time. How many times did she hit the ball?

_____

---

3. Complete the "What's My Rule?" table and state the rule.

in	out
1	$\frac{1}{5}$
3	
	5
	1
	0

Rule

4. One quart of ice cream serves about 8 people.

a. About how many people will 12 quarts of ice cream serve?

_____

b. About how many quarts are needed to serve 180 people?

_____

---

5. Solve.

a. If 15 marbles are $\frac{3}{5}$ of the marbles in a bag, how many marbles are in the bag?

_____

b. If 14 pennies are 7% of a pile of pennies, how many pennies are in the pile?

_____

c. 75 students are absent today. This is 10% of the students enrolled in the school. How many students are enrolled in the school?

_____

d. Jane paid $90 for a new radio. It was on sale for $\frac{3}{4}$ of the regular price. What is the regular price of the radio?

_____

Sources

Unit 7

Augarde, Tony. *The Oxford Guide to Word Games.* New York: Oxford University Press, 1986.

Beckmann, Petr. *A History of π.* New York: Golem Press, 1971.

Diagram Group. *Comparisons.* New York: St. Martin's Press, 1980.

University of Tokyo—http://www.cecm.sfu.ca/personal/jborwein/Kanada_50b.html

The World Almanac® and *Book of Facts.* Mahwah, N.J.: World Almanac, 1997.

WuDunn, Sheryl. "Chinese Buy American Dream by the Inch." *New York Times,* January 29, 1993, p. 1.

Unit 8

Britannica Online—http://www.eb.com

Dennis, Jerry. *It's Raining Frogs and Fishes: Four Seasons of Natural Phenomena and Oddities of the Sky.* New York: HarperPerennial Library, 1992.

Games Magazine.

The Guinness Book of Records 1993. New York: Facts on File, 1992.

Lyon, Ron and Jenny Paschall. *Beyond Belief!!: Bizarre Facts and Incredible Stories from All Over the World.* New York: Villard Books, 1993.

Schlissel, Lillian. *Women's Diaries of the Westward Journey.* New York: Schocken Books, 1982.

Sources (continued)

Unit 9

Ash, Russell. *The Top 10 of Everything.* New York: Dorling Kindersley, 1994.

Caldwell, Otis and Stuart Courtis. *Then and Now in Education, 1845–1923.* Yonkers on Hudson, NY: World Book Co., 1924.

Cohen, Patricia Cline. *A Calculating People: The Spread of Numeracy in Early America.* Chicago: University of Chicago Press, 1982.

Fuller, Wayne E. *One-Room Schools of the Middle West.* Lawrence, Kans: University of Kansas Press, 1994.

Levey, Judith S., ed. *The World Almanac for Kids,* 1996. Mahwah, N.J.: Funk & Wagnalls Corporation, 1995.

National Center for Education Statistics. *The State of Mathematics Achievement.* Washington, D.C.: Government Printing Office.

Peterson, I. "Lucky Choice Turns Up World-Record Prime." *Science News,* Vol. 152, September 13, 1997, p. 164.

Unit 11

Ash, Russell. *The Top 10 of Everything.* New York: Dorling Kindersley, 1994.

Britannica Online—http://www.eb.com

Donley, Richard E. *Everything Has Its Price.* New York: Simon and Schuster, 1995.

Houwink, R. *The Odd Book of Data.* New York: Elsevier Publishing Company, 1965.

Krantz, Les. *America by the Numbers: Facts and Figures from the Weighty to the Way Out.* Boston: Houghton Mifflin, 1983.

Lord, John. *Sizes.* New York: HarperPerennial, 1995.

Louis, David. *2201 Fascinating Facts.* New York: Greenwich House, 1983.

Lyon, Ron and Jenny Paschall. *Beyond Belief!!: Bizarre Facts and Incredible Stories from All Over the World.* New York: Villard Books, 1993.

Mottershead, Lorraine. *Metamorphosis.* Palo Alto, Calif: Dale Seymour Publications, 1977.

Seuling, Barbara. *You Can't Count a Billion Dollars.* New York: Doubleday and Company, 1979.

Glossary

abundant number A number for which the sum of all the proper factors is greater than the number itself. For example, 12 is an abundant number because the sum of its proper factors is $1 + 2 + 3 + 4 + 6 = 16$, and 16 is greater than 12. *See also* deficient number, perfect number, *and* proper factor.

account (bank) balance The amount of money in a bank account at a given time. *See also* "in the black" *and* "in the red."

acre A unit of area equal to 43,560 square feet.

algebraic expression An expression that contains a variable. For example, if Maria is 2 inches taller than Joe, and if the variable *M* represents Maria's height, then the expression $M - 2$ represents Joe's height. *See also* expression.

algorithm A set of step-by-step instructions for doing something—carrying out a computation, solving a problem, and so forth.

angle A figure that is formed by two rays with a common endpoint. The common endpoint is called the vertex of the angle. An acute angle has a measure greater than 0° and less than 90°. An obtuse angle has a measure greater than 90° and less than 180°. A right angle measures 90°. A straight angle measures 180°. *See also* endpoint *and* ray.

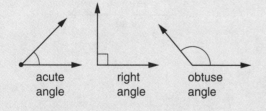

| acute angle | right angle | obtuse angle |

angle of separation A measure of how far fingers can be spread apart. Shown is the angle of separation between a person's thumb and first finger.

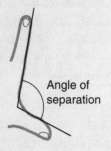

Angle of separation

angle, reflex An angle whose measure is between 180° and 360°.

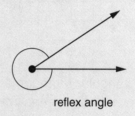

reflex angle

angles, adjacent Two angles that share a common side, but which do not otherwise overlap. In the diagram, Angles 1 and 2 are adjacent angles. So are Angles 2 and 3, Angles 3 and 4, and Angles 4 and 1.

angles, vertical Angles that are formed by two intersecting lines but have no sides in common. In the diagram above, Angles 2 and 4 are vertical angles. Their measures are equal. Similarly, Angles 1 and 3 are vertical angles.

apex In a pyramid or cone, the vertex opposite the base.

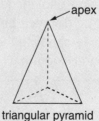

apex

triangular pyramid

area The measure of the surface inside a closed boundary. The formula for the area of a rectangle is $A = l * w$ where A represents the area, l the length, and w the width. The formula may also be expressed as $A = b * h$, where b represents the length of the base and h the height of the rectangle.

area model A model for multiplication problems, in which the length and width of a rectangle represent the factors and the area represents the product.

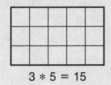

$$3 * 5 = 15$$

array A rectangular arrangement of objects in rows and columns in which each row has the same number of parts and each column has the same number of parts.

axis Either of the two number lines used to form a coordinate grid.

bar graph A graph in which horizontal or vertical bars represent data.

base In exponential notation, a number that is used as a repeated factor. In the expression 2^3, 2 is the base and is used as a factor 3 times.

base of a parallelogram One of the sides of a parallelogram; also, the length of this side. The shortest distance between the base and the side opposite the base is the height of the parallelogram.

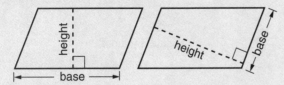

base of a polygon The side on which the polygon "sits"; the side that is perpendicular to the height of the polygon.

base of a polyhedron, cone, or cylinder One face or one of a pair of parallel faces. The height is the length of a line segment perpendicular to a base of the figure that extends from that base to an opposite face or vertex.

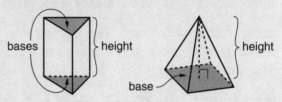

base of a rectangle One of the sides of a rectangle; also, the length of this side. The length of the side perpendicular to the base is the height of the rectangle.

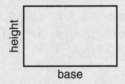

base of a triangle One of the sides of a triangle; also, the length of this side. The shortest distance between the base and the vertex opposite the base is the height of the triangle.

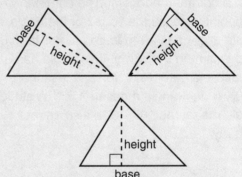

calibrate To divide or mark to show measurements, as on a graduated cylinder.

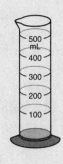

capacity A measure of how much liquid or other pourable substance a container can hold. *See also* volume.

carbon dioxide One of the body's waste products; removed by the blood and expelled from the lungs.

cardiac output A rate that represents the amount of blood the heart pumps per minute. It is calculated by multiplying the amount of blood pumped per beat times the heart rate.

change-of-sign or OPP key The [+↺−] key on the calculator used to change a positive to a negative number or a negative to a positive number.

circle (pie) graph A graph in which a circle and its interior are divided into parts to represent the parts of a set of data. The circle represents the whole set of data.

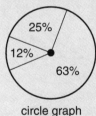

circle graph

circumference The distance around a circle or sphere. The perimeter of a circle.

common denominator A number that is a multiple of each denominator in a given set of fractions.

composite number A whole number that has more than two whole-number factors. For example, 10 is a composite number because it has more than two factors: 1, 2, 5, and 10. A composite number is divisible by at least three whole numbers. *See also* prime number.

cone A 3-dimensional shape having a circular base, a curved surface, and one vertex.

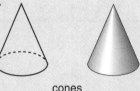

cones

congruent Two figures that are identical in size and shape are called *congruent figures.* If you put one on top of the other, they match exactly. Congruent figures are also said to be *congruent to* each other.

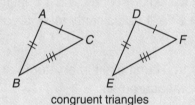

congruent triangles

contour line A curve on a map through places where a measurement (for example, temperature, elevation, or growing season) is the same. Often a contour line separates regions that have been colored differently on the map to show a range of conditions.

control cable On a bicycle, the cable that connects the shifter to the gear.

coordinate A number used to locate a point on a number line, or either of two numbers used to locate a point on a coordinate grid.

coordinate grid A device for locating points in a plane by means of ordered number pairs or coordinates. A rectangular coordinate grid is formed by two number lines that intersect at right angles at their zero points.

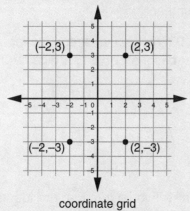

coordinate grid

cube *See* regular polyhedron.

cubic centimeter (cm³) A metric unit of volume; the volume of a cube 1 centimeter on each side. 1 cubic centimeter is equal to 1 milliliter.

cubic unit A unit used in a volume and capacity measurement.

cubit An ancient unit of length, measured from the point of the elbow to the end of the middle finger, or about 18 inches. The Latin word *cubitum* means "elbow."

curved surface A surface that is rounded rather than flat.

cylinder A 3-dimensional shape having a curved surface and parallel circular bases that are the same size. A can is a common object shaped like a cylinder.

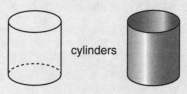

cylinders

deficient number A number for which the sum of all the proper factors is less than the number. For example, 10 is a deficient number because the sum of its proper factors is 1 + 2 + 5 = 8, and 8 is less than 10. *See also* abundant number, perfect number, and proper factor.

degree (°) A unit of measure for angles based on dividing a circle into 360 equal parts. Also, a unit of measure for temperature.

denominator The number of equal parts into which the whole (or ONE or unit) is divided. In the fraction $\frac{a}{b}$, b is the denominator. *See also* numerator.

density A measure of the mass (weight) of an object or substance for a given unit of volume. In the metric system, the density of water is 1 gram per cubic centimeter. The density of an object can be calculated by dividing its mass by its volume.

diameter A line segment that passes through the center of a circle (or sphere) and has endpoints on the circle (or sphere); also, the length of such a line segment. The diameter of a circle is twice its radius.

difference *See* subtraction.

digit In the base-ten numeration system, one of the symbols 0, 1, 2, 3, 4, 5, 6, 7, 8, 9. Digits can be used to write any number. For example, the numeral 145 is made up of the digits 1, 4, and 5.

dimension A measure in one direction— for example, length or width.

discount The amount by which the regular price of an item is reduced.

displacement A movement of something out of its original place.

dividend *See* division.

divisibility test A test to determine whether a whole number is divisible by another whole number, without actually doing the division.

divisible by One whole number is divisible by another whole number if the result of the division is a whole number (with a remainder of zero). For example, 28 is divisible by 7, because 28 divided by 7 is 4 with a remainder of zero.

division A mathematical operation based on "sharing" or "separating into equal parts." The dividend is the total before sharing. The divisor is the number of equal parts or the number in each equal part. The quotient is the result of division. For example, in 28/7 = 4, 28 is the dividend, 7 is the divisor, and 4 is the quotient. The number left over when a set of objects is shared equally or separated into equal groups is called the remainder. For 29/7, the quotient is 4 and the remainder is 1. Multiplication "undoes" division: 28/7 = 4, and 4 ∗ 7 = 28.

dividend/divisor = quotient

$$\frac{dividend}{divisor} = quotient$$

divisor *See* division.

dodecahedron *See* regular polyhedron.

edge A line segment where two faces of a polyhedron meet.

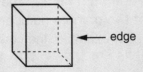
← edge

electoral votes The number of votes a state can cast (based on its number of representatives and senators) for a presidential candidate.

endpoint The point at either end of a line segment; also, the point at the end of a ray. Endpoints are used to name line segments; for example, segment *TL* or segment *LT* names a line segment between and including points *T* and *L*. *See also* ray.

enlarge To increase the size of an object or shape.

equally likely Events that have the same chance of occurring.

equation A mathematical sentence that states the equality of two quantities.

equivalent fractions Fractions that have different numerators and denominators but name the same number. For example, $\frac{1}{2}$ and $\frac{4}{8}$ are equivalent fractions.

even number A whole number such as 2, 4, 6, and so forth that can be evenly divided by 2 (divided by 2 with 0 remainder). *See also* odd number.

exponent *See* exponential notation.

exponential notation A shorthand way of representing repeated multiplication of the same factor. For example, 2^3 is exponential notation for 2 ∗ 2 ∗ 2. The small, raised 3, called the exponent, indicates how many times the number 2, called the base, is used as a factor.

expression A group of mathematical symbols (numbers, operation signs, variables, grouping symbols) that represent a number—or can represent a number if values are assigned to any variables it contains.

face A surface on a 3-dimensional figure.

face
triangular pyramid

factor A number that is multiplied by another number. For example, 4 and 3 are factors of 12, because 4 ∗ 3 = 12.

factor pair Two whole-number factors of a number *n* whose product is the number *n*. A number may have more than one factor pair. For example, the factor pairs for 21 are 1 and 21, and 3 and 7.

factor rainbow A way of showing factor pairs in a list of all the factors of a number. This display can be helpful in checking whether a list of factors is correct.

factors of 24

factor string A name for a number written as a product of at least two whole-number factors. For example, a factor string for the number 24 is 2 * 3 * 4. This factor string has three factors, so its length is 3. The number 1 is never part of a factor string.

factor tree A method used to obtain the prime factorization of a number. The original number is represented as a product of factors, and each of those factors is represented as a product of factors, and so on, until the factor string consists of prime numbers.

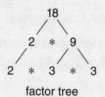
factor tree

fair game A game in which each player has the same chance of winning. If any player has an advantage or disadvantage (for example, by playing first), then the game is not fair.

fathom A unit used mainly by people who work with boats and ships to measure depths under water and lengths of cables and cords. A fathom is now defined as a length of 6 feet.

formula A general rule for finding the value of something. A formula is often written in abbreviated form with letters, called *variables.* For example, a formula for distance traveled can be written as $d = r * t,$ where the variable *d* stands for distance, *r* for speed, and *t* for time.

fraction A number in the form $\frac{a}{b}$ or *a/b,* where *a* and *b* are whole numbers and *b* is not 0. Fractions are used to name part of a whole or part of a whole collection of objects, or to compare two quantities. A fraction can represent division; for example, $\frac{2}{3}$ can be thought of as 2 divided by 3.

gear On a bicycle, a disk with teeth rotated by the pedals.

gear ratio On a bicycle, the ratio of the number of teeth on the rear-wheel gear to the number of teeth on the pedal gear.

gear system On a bicycle, the gears, chains, cables, and shifters that allow the rider to set the gear ratio.

geometric solid A 3-dimensional shape bounded by surfaces. Common geometric solids include the rectangular prism, square pyramid, cylinder, cone, and sphere. Despite its name, a geometric solid is "hollow"; it does not include the points in its interior.

great span The distance from the tip of the thumb to the tip of the fourth (little) finger, stretched as far as possible.

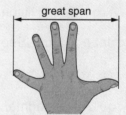
great span

greatest common factor The largest factor that two or more numbers have in common. For example, the common factors of 24 and 36 are 1, 2, 3, 4, 6, and 12. The greatest common factor of 36 and 24 is 12.

heart rate The number of times per minute a heart beats.

height of a parallelogram *See* base of a parallelogram.

height of a polyhedron, cone, or cylinder *See* base of a polyhedron, cone, or cylinder.

height of a rectangle *See* base of a rectangle.

height of a triangle *See* base of a triangle.

hexagon A polygon with 6 sides.

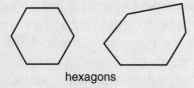
hexagons

horizontal Positioned in a left-right orientation; parallel to the horizon.

icon A small picture or diagram, sometimes used to represent a quantity. For example, an icon of a stadium might be used to represent 100,000 people on a pictograph.

improper fraction *See* top-heavy fraction.

"in the black" You have more money than you owe. A positive account balance.

"in the red" You owe more money than you have. A negative account balance.

inscribed polygon A polygon all of whose vertices are points on a circle or other figure.

inscribed square

interior The set of all points in a plane "inside" a closed 2-dimensional figure, such as a polygon or circle. Also, the set of all points in space "inside" a closed 3-dimensional figure, such as a polyhedron or sphere. The interior is usually not considered to be part of the figure.

intersect To meet (at a point, line, and so on).

kite A quadrilateral with exactly two pairs of adjacent, congruent sides. (A rhombus is not a kite.)

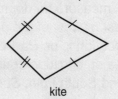
kite

landmark A measure of data. Landmarks include *median, mode, maximum, minimum,* and *range.*

latitude The measure of an angle whose vertex is the center of the Earth; used to indicate the location of a place with reference to the equator. *See also* longitude.

line (broken-line) graph A graph in which points are connected by a line or line segments to represent data.

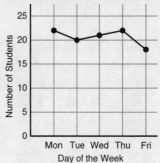

line plot A sketch of data in which check marks, X's, or other marks above a number line show the frequency of each value.

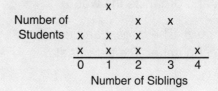

line segment A straight path joining two points, called *endpoints,* of the line segment.

liter (L) A metric unit of capacity equal to the volume of a cube 10 centimeters on a side. 1 L = 1000 mL = 1000 cm^3. A liter is a little larger than a quart. *See also* milliliter (mL).

longitude A measure (in degrees) of how far east or west of the prime meridian a location is on Earth; determined by semicircles of longitude connecting the North Pole and South Pole. *See also* latitude.

magnitude estimate An estimate of the size of a numerical result—whether it is in the tens, hundreds, thousands, and so on.

magnitude increase A 10-fold increase in a value.

majority More than one-half of a count.

map direction symbol A symbol on a map that identifies north, south, east, and west. Sometimes only north is indicated.

map legend (map key) A diagram that explains the symbols, markings, and colors on a map.

map scale A rate that compares the distance between two locations on a map with the actual distance between them. The rate is often represented by a labeled line segment, similar to a ruler.

mathematics A study of relationships among numbers, shapes, and patterns. Mathematics is used to count and measure things, to discover similarities and differences, to solve problems, and to learn about and organize the world.

maximum The largest amount; the greatest number in a set of data.

mean A typical or middle value for a set of numbers. It is found by adding the numbers in the set and then dividing the sum by the number of numbers. It is often referred to as the *average.*

median The middle value in a set of data when the data are listed in order from smallest to largest (or largest to smallest). If there is an even number of data points, the median is the mean of the two middle values.

metric system of measurement A measurement system based on the base-ten numeration system and used in most countries in the world. Units for linear measure (length, distance) include millimeter, centimeter, meter, and kilometer; units for mass (weight) include gram and kilogram; units for capacity (amount of liquid or other pourable substance a container can hold) include milliliter and liter.

milliliter (mL) A metric unit of volume or capacity equal to 1 cubic centimeter. There are 1000 milliliters in a liter.

minimum The smallest amount; the least number in a set of data.

minuend *See* subtraction.

mixed number A number that is equal to the sum of a whole number and a fraction. For example, $2\frac{1}{4}$ is equal to $2 + \frac{1}{4}$.

modal The adjective form of the word *mode.*

mode The value or values that occur most often in a set of data.

multiple of a number n The product of a whole number and the number n. For example, the numbers 2, 4, 6, 8, and 10 are all multiples of 2 because $2 * 1 = 2; 2 * 2 = 4; 2 * 3 = 6;$ and so on.

multiplication A mathematical operation used to find the total number of things in several equal groups, or to find the number that is *x* times another number. Numbers being multiplied are called factors. The result of multiplication is called the product. In $5 * 12 = 60$, 5 and 12 are factors, and 60 is the product. Division "undoes" multiplication; $60/5 = 12$, and $12 * 5 = 60$.

name-collection box A box-like diagram containing a number, used for collecting equivalent names for that number.

natural fathom A measure found by having a person stretch out both arms so that the hands are as far apart as possible. For most people, the distance is about the same as their height.

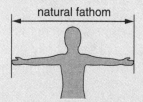
natural fathom

normal span The distance from the tip of the thumb to the tip of the first (index) finger, stretched as far apart as possible.

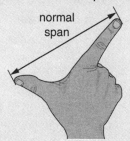
normal span

number model A number sentence that shows how the parts of a number story are related. For example: $5 + 8 = 13$; $27 - 11 = 16$; $3 * 30 = 90$; $56/8 = 7$.

number sentence A sentence that is made up of numerals and a relation symbol (such as $=, <, >, \neq, \leq,$ and $\geq$). Most number sentences also contain at least one operation symbol. Number sentences may also have grouping symbols, such as parentheses.

numerator In a whole divided into a number of equal parts, the numerator is the number of equal parts being considered. In the fraction $\frac{a}{b}$, *a* is the numerator. *See also* denominator.

nutrients Nourishing substances that the blood distributes throughout the body.

odd number A whole number that is not divisible by 2, such as 1, 3, 5, and so forth. When an odd number is divided by 2, the remainder is 1. A whole number is either an odd number or an even number.

opposite of a number A number that is the same distance from zero on the number line as the given number, but on the opposite side of zero. For example, the opposite of $+3$ is -3; the opposite of -5 is $+5$.

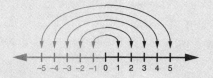

ordered number pair Two numbers in a specific order used to locate a point on a coordinate grid. They are usually written inside parentheses: (2,3).

organizing data Arranging and presenting data in a way that makes the data easier to understand.

oxygen An essential element that the blood takes from the lungs and distributes throughout the body.

parallel lines (segments, rays) Lines (segments, rays) that are the same distance apart and never meet.

parallelogram A quadrilateral that has two pairs of parallel sides. Pairs of opposite sides of a parallelogram are congruent.

parallelogram

pedal gear On a bicycle, the gear attached to the pedal.

pendulum A weighted string or wire, suspended from a fixed support, that can swing freely back and forth under the influence of gravity.

percent (%) Per hundred, or out of a hundred. For example, "48% of the students in the school are boys" means that out of every 100 students in the school, 48 are boys.

perfect number A number whose proper factors have a sum equal to the number itself. 6 is a perfect number because the sum of its proper factors is $1 + 2 + 3 = 6$. *See also* abundant number, deficient number, and proper factor.

perimeter The distance around a 2-dimensional shape. A formula for the perimeter of a rectangle is $P = 2 * (l + w)$, where l represents the length and w the width of the rectangle.

perpendicular Two rays, lines, or line segments that form right angles are perpendicular. The symbol [⊥] represents "is perpendicular to"

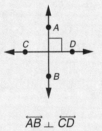

$\overleftrightarrow{AB} \perp \overleftrightarrow{CD}$

perspective drawing In this type of drawing, parallel lines that move away from the viewer are drawn so that they come together at a vanishing point. The proportions in a perspective drawing are not the same as the proportions of the actual object.

pi (π) The ratio of the circumference of a circle to its diameter. Pi is the same for every circle, approximately 3.14. Also written as the Greek letter π.

pictograph A graph constructed with pictures or icons, which make it possible to visualize at a glance the ratios between two counts or measures. Sometimes called icon graph.

place value Determines the value of a digit in a number, written in standard notation, as determined by its position. Each place has a value ten times that of the place to its right and one-tenth the value of the place to its left.

plane A flat surface that extends forever.

polygon A closed 2-dimensional figure consisting of line segments (sides) connected endpoint to endpoint. The interior of a polygon consists of all the points of the plane "inside" the polygon.

polyhedron A 3-dimensional shape, all of whose surfaces (faces) are flat. Each face consists of a polygon and the interior of the polygon. *See also* regular polyhedron.

population In data collection, the target audience for a given survey.

population density The number of people living in a given area; usually given as a rate, such as "1000 people per square mile."

power of a number Usually, a product of factors that are all the same. $5 * 5 * 5$ (or 125) is called 5 to the third power or the third power of 5, because 5 is a factor three times. $5 * 5 * 5$ can also be written as 5^3, in which the superscript 3 represents the "power" of 5.

power of 10 A whole number that can be written using only 10s as factors. For example, 100 is equal to $10 * 10$ or 10^2. 100 is the second power of 10.

powers key The [y^x] key on the calculator, used to calculate powers. By pressing 4, [y^x], and 5, in that order, one obtains the fifth power of 4, or 4^5, which equals 1024.

prime factorization A number expressed as a product of prime factors. For example, the prime factorization of 24 is $2 * 2 * 2 * 3$.

prime meridian An imaginary semicircle on the Earth connecting the North Pole and South Pole through Greenwich, England. *See also* longitude.

prime number A whole number greater than 1 that has exactly two whole-number factors, 1 and itself. For example, 7 is a prime number because its only two factors are 1 and 7. A prime number is divisible only by 1 and itself. The first five prime numbers are 2, 3, 5, 7, and 11. *See also* composite number.

prism A polyhedron with two parallel faces, called bases, that are the same size and shape. Prisms are classified according to the shape of two parallel bases. The faces of a prism are always bounded by parallelograms, and are often rectangular.

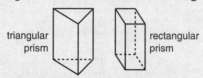

triangular prism   rectangular prism

probability A number from 0 to 1 that indicates the likelihood that something (an event) will happen. The closer a probability is to 1, the more likely it is that an event will happen.

product *See* multiplication.

profile A general description or view. A profile can be in many different forms, including a graph.

proper factor Any whole-number factor of a number except the number itself. The factors of 10 are 1, 2, 5, and 10. The proper factors of 10 are 1, 2, and 5.

pulse Expansion and contraction of the arteries caused by the beating of the heart; usually detected on the wrist or neck.

pulse rate The number of times per minute the arteries beat with a pulse.

pyramid A polyhedron in which one face (the base) is a polygon and the other faces are formed by triangles with a common vertex (the apex). A pyramid is classified according to the shape of its base.

square pyramid

quadrangle (quadrilateral) A polygon with 4 sides.

quotient *See* division.

radius A line segment from the center of a circle (or sphere) to any point on the circle (or sphere); also, the length of such a line segment.

random number A number that has the same chance of appearing as any other number.

range The difference between the maximum and minimum in a set of data.

rate A comparison of two quantities with unlike units. For example, a speed such as 55 miles per hour compares distance with time.

ratio A comparison of two quantities with like units. Ratios can be expressed with fractions, decimals, percents, or words; or they can be written with a colon between the two numbers being compared. For example, if a team wins 3 games out of 5 games played, the ratio of wins to total games is 3/5, 0.6, 60%, 3 to 5, or 3:5 (read "three to five").

ray A straight path that extends infinitely from a point, called its *endpoint*.

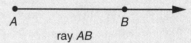

ray *AB*

reaction time The amount of time it takes to respond to a stimulus.

rear-wheel gear On a bicycle, the gear attached to the rear wheel.

rectangular land survey system A land survey that uses reference lines parallel to the north-south meridians of longitude and the east-west parallels of latitude to divide the land. It outlines pieces of land shaped like rectangles.

rectangular method A method for finding area, in which rectangles are used to surround a figure or parts of a figure. All the areas that are calculated are either areas of rectangles or of triangular halves of rectangular regions

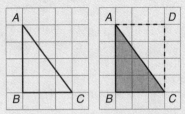

The area of rectangle *ABCD* is 3 units ∗ 4 units = 12 square units. The area of triangle *ABC* is one half the area of the rectangle, or 6 square units.

reduce To make an object or shape smaller.

regular polygon A convex polygon in which all sides are the same length and all angles have the same measure.

regular polyhedron A polyhedron with faces that are all congruent regular polygons. There are five regular polyhedrons:

tetrahedron	4 faces, each formed by an equilateral triangle
cube	6 faces, each formed by a square
octahedron	8 faces, each formed by an equilateral triangle
dodecahedron	12 faces, each formed by a regular pentagon
icosahedron	20 faces, each formed by an equilateral triangle

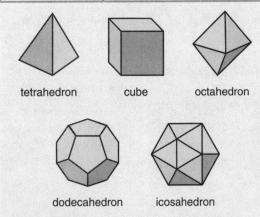

tetrahedron   cube   octahedron

dodecahedron   icosahedron

regular tessellation A tessellation made up of only one kind of regular polygon.

remainder *See* division.

rhombus A parallelogram whose sides are all the same length. The angles are usually not right angles, but they may be right angles.

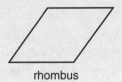

rhombus

sample A subset of a population used to represent the whole population.

scale The ratio of the distance on a map, globe, or drawing to the actual distance.

scale drawing An accurate picture of an object in which all parts are drawn to the same scale. For example, if an actual object measured 33 by 22 yards, a scale drawing of it might measure 33 by 22 millimeters.

scientific notation A system for representing numbers in which a number is written as the product of a power of 10 and a number that is at least 1 but less than 10. Scientific notation allows for writing big and small numbers with only a few symbols. For example, 4,000,000 in scientific notation is $4 * 10^6$.

section of land A land unit equal to one square mile, 640 acres, or $\frac{1}{36}$ of a township.

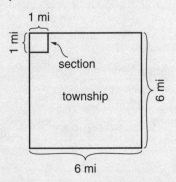

shifter On a bicycle, the lever that enables the rider to change gears.

similar figures Figures that are exactly the same shape but not necessarily the same size.

simplest form A fraction in which the numerator and denominator have no common factors except 1 and the numerator is less than the denominator. Also, a mixed number in which the fraction is in simplest form.

simulation An activity in which an object or event is represented by something else.

slide rule A device used to perform calculations.

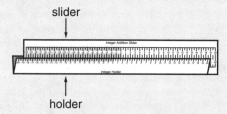
slider

holder

span *See* normal span *or* great span.

speed A rate that describes the relationship between distance traveled and the time it takes to travel that distance.

sphere The set of all points in space that are a given distance (the radius of the sphere) from a given point (the center of the sphere). A ball is shaped like a sphere, as is Earth.

center • radius
sphere

square number A number that is the product of a whole number multiplied by itself; a whole number to the second power. For example 25 is a square number because 25 = 5 * 5. A square number can be represented by a square array.

square root of a number The square root of a number *n* is the number that, when multiplied by itself, results in the number *n*. The square root of 16 is 4 because 4 * 4 = 16.

square unit A unit used in area measurement.

standard notation The most familiar way of representing whole numbers, integers, and decimals by writing digits in specified places.

stem-and-leaf plot A display of data in which digits with larger place values are named *stems,* and digits with smaller place values are named *leaves.*

Stems	Leaves					
10s	1s					
2	4	4	5	6	7	7	8
3	1	1	2	2	6	6	6
4	1	1	3	5	8	
5	0	2				

stimulus Something that causes a response or reaction. A green traffic light is the stimulus for drivers that causes the response of cars moving.

subtraction A mathematical operation based on "taking away" or comparing "how much more?". The number being subtracted is called the *subtrahend;* the number it is subtracted from is called the *minuend;* the result of subtraction is called the *difference.* In 45 − 12 = 33, 45 is the minuend, 12 is the subtrahend, and 33 is the difference. Addition "undoes" subtraction: 45 − 12 = 33, and 12 + 33 = 45.

subtrahend *See* subtraction.

survey A study that collects data from human respondents. Surveys are used to find out about people's characteristics, behaviors, interests, and so on.

target heart rate The number of heartbeats per minute recommended while exercising. (Varies from individual to individual.)

tessellation An arrangement of closed shapes that covers a surface completely without overlaps or gaps. *See also* tile.

tile A shape used in a tessellation. If only one shape is repeated in a tessellation, the tessellation is called a *same-tile tessellation*.

tiling Covering a surface with uniform shapes so there are no gaps or overlaps, except possibly gaps around the edges.

top-heavy fraction A fraction that names a number greater than or equal to 1; a fraction whose numerator is greater than or equal to its denominator. For example, $\frac{7}{3}$, $\frac{5}{5}$, and $\frac{16}{4}$. Also called improper fractions.

township A square land unit 6 miles on each side (having an area of 36 square miles). *See also* section of land.

trapezoid A quadrilateral that has exactly one pair of parallel sides. No two sides need to be the same length.

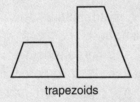

trapezoids

triangle A polygon with 3 sides and 3 angles. An equilateral triangle has 3 sides of the same length. An isosceles triangle has 2 sides of the same length. A scalene triangle has no sides of the same length.

twin primes Two prime numbers that are separated by just one composite number. For example, 3 and 5 are twin primes because they are separated by the composite number 4. The numbers 11 and 13 are also twin primes.

unit ONE of something.

unit fraction A fraction that names one of the equal parts of the whole (in the form $\frac{1}{n}$). For example, $\frac{1}{2}$, $\frac{1}{3}$, $\frac{1}{8}$, $\frac{1}{12}$, and $\frac{1}{20}$ are unit fractions.

unit percent One percent (1%).

unit price The cost for one item.

unlike denominators Denominators that are different, as in $\frac{1}{2}$ and $\frac{1}{3}$.

variable A letter or other symbol that represents a number. A variable need not represent one specific number; it can stand for many different values.

vertex The point at which the rays of an angle, two sides of a polygon, or two edges of a polyhedron meet.

vertices Plural of *vertex*.

vertices

volume The measure of the amount of space occupied by a 3-dimensional object.

whole The entire object, collection of objects, or quantity being considered; the ONE, the unit, 100%.

Cash and IOU Cards

+	+	−	−
$1 Cash	**$1 Cash**	**$1 IOU Debt**	**$1 IOU Debt**
+	+	−	−
$1 Cash	**$1 Cash**	**$1 IOU Debt**	**$1 IOU Debt**
+	+	−	−
$1 Cash	**$1 Cash**	**$1 IOU Debt**	**$1 IOU Debt**
+	+	−	−
$1 Cash	**$1 Cash**	**$1 IOU Debt**	**$1 IOU Debt**
+	+	−	−
$1 Cash	**$1 Cash**	**$1 IOU Debt**	**$1 IOU Debt**

Use with Lesson 77 and following.

Build-It Card Deck

$\dfrac{5}{9}$	$\dfrac{1}{3}$	$\dfrac{11}{12}$	$\dfrac{1}{12}$
$\dfrac{7}{12}$	$\dfrac{3}{8}$	$\dfrac{1}{4}$	$\dfrac{1}{5}$
$\dfrac{2}{3}$	$\dfrac{3}{7}$	$\dfrac{4}{7}$	$\dfrac{3}{4}$
$\dfrac{3}{5}$	$\dfrac{4}{5}$	$\dfrac{7}{9}$	$\dfrac{5}{6}$

Algebra Election Cards, Set 1

What is the value of n?

$-20 + x = n$

$-100 + (-x) = n$

What is the value of n?

$20 + (-x) = n$

$-20 - (-x) = n$

Which is greater:

x^2 or 10^3?

x^3 or 10^4?

Which is less:

$\frac{x^3}{10}$ or $(x + 10)^2$?

$10 * x^2$ or $(x + 10)^3$?

Complete:

$x * 10^6 = $ ——— million

$x * 10^9 = $ ——— billion

$x * 10^{12} = $ ——— ———

What is the value of n?

$n = ((5 * x) - 4)/2$

Suppose you earn x dollars per hour. Complete the table.

Time	Earnings
1 hr	$
2 hr	$
4 hr	$
10 hr	$

A boulder dropped off a cliff falls approximately $16 * x^2$ feet in x seconds. How many feet is that?

Find:

x squared

x to the fourth power

$1/x$

Find n. (*Hint:* n could be a negative number.)

$1000 - n = x$

$1000 + n = -x$

Insert parentheses in

$10 * x - 10$

so that its value is greater than 0 and less than 100.

Find n. (*Hint:* n could be a negative number.)

$n + 10 = x$

$n - 10 = x$

Find n.

$n = (2 * x)/10$

$n + 1 = (2 * x)$

$T = B - (2 * \frac{H}{1000})$

If $B = 80$ and $H = 100x$, what does T equal?

Which number is this?

$x * 10^2$?

$x * 10^5$?

Tell whether each is true or false.

$10 * x > 100$

$\frac{1}{2} * x * 100 < 10^3$

$x^3 * 1000 > 4 * 10^4$

Algebra Election Cards, Set 2

What is n?

$$5 + 2 * x = n + x$$

$x + \triangle$ | 200 oz

1 $\triangle$ weighs _____ ounces

Insert parentheses so that the equation is true.

$$10 * x + 4 = 10 * x + 40$$

Is point (x,x) above, below, or on the line through points A and B?

$A\,(0,30)$ $B\,(60,30)$

Tell which is correct for each: $<$, $=$, or $>$.

$x\ \ <\ =\ >\ \ 30 - x$

$x\ \ <\ =\ >\ \ 20 - x$

$x\ \ <\ =\ >\ \ 10 - x$

Name a number n such that $x - n$ is a negative number greater than -10.

Suppose you have 10 $\boxed{+}$ markers and $2 * x$ $\boxed{-}$ markers.

What is your balance?

Suppose you have x $\boxed{+}$ markers and 40 $\boxed{-}$ markers.

What is your balance?

Is point (x,x) to the left of, to the right of, or on the line through points A and B?

$A\,(30,0)$ $B\,(30,60)$

What is the value of n?

$$10 + (-x) = n$$

$$-10 - (-x) = n$$

What is the median of 4, 8, 12, 13, and x?

If $(2 * x) + n = 100$, what is the value of n?

Is $1/x$ greater than, less than, or equal to $\frac{1}{10}$?

Subtract.

$$x - 100 = ?$$

$$x - (-100) = ?$$

Add.

$$-25 + x = ?$$

$$x + 3 - 10 = ?$$

Suppose you travel x miles per hour. Complete the table.

Time	Distance
1 hr	
2 hr	
4 hr	
10 hr	

Fraction Action, Fraction Friction Card Deck

$\dfrac{1}{2}$	$\dfrac{1}{3}$	$\dfrac{2}{3}$	$\dfrac{1}{4}$
$\dfrac{3}{4}$	$\dfrac{1}{6}$	$\dfrac{1}{6}$	$\dfrac{5}{6}$
$\dfrac{1}{12}$	$\dfrac{1}{12}$	$\dfrac{5}{12}$	$\dfrac{5}{12}$
$\dfrac{7}{12}$	$\dfrac{7}{12}$	$\dfrac{11}{12}$	$\dfrac{11}{12}$

Use with Lesson 96.

Square Tiles

Shape Cards

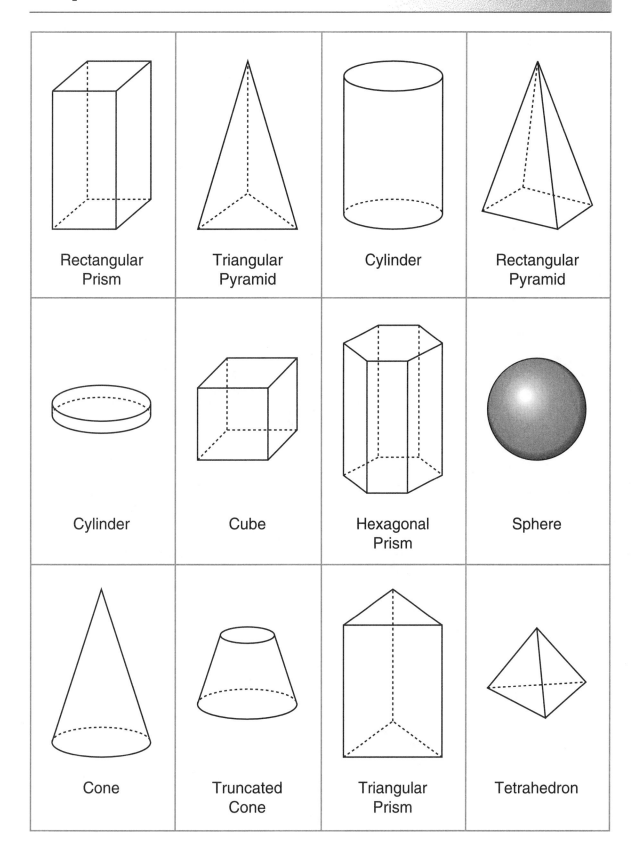

Rectangular Prism	Triangular Pyramid	Cylinder	Rectangular Pyramid
Cylinder	Cube	Hexagonal Prism	Sphere
Cone	Truncated Cone	Triangular Prism	Tetrahedron

Property Cards

I have an even number of vertices.	I have no vertices.	I have at least 2 edges that are parallel to each other.	I have an odd number of edges.
One of my vertices is formed by an even number of edges.	I have at least one curved edge.	I have fewer than 6 vertices.	I have at least 2 edges that are perpendicular to each other.
All of my surfaces are polygons.	I have at least one face (flat surface).	I have at least one curved surface.	All of my faces are triangles.
All of my faces are regular polygons.	At least one of my faces is a circle.	I have at least one pair of faces that are parallel to each other.	**Wild Card:** Pick your own surface property.

Use with Lesson 104.

Vertex/Edge	Vertex/Edge	Vertex/Edge	Vertex/Edge
Vertex/Edge	Vertex/Edge	Vertex/Edge	Vertex/Edge
Surface	Surface	Surface	Surface
Surface	Surface	Surface	Surface

50-mL Measuring Cone

See the back of this page or Master 78 for instructions.

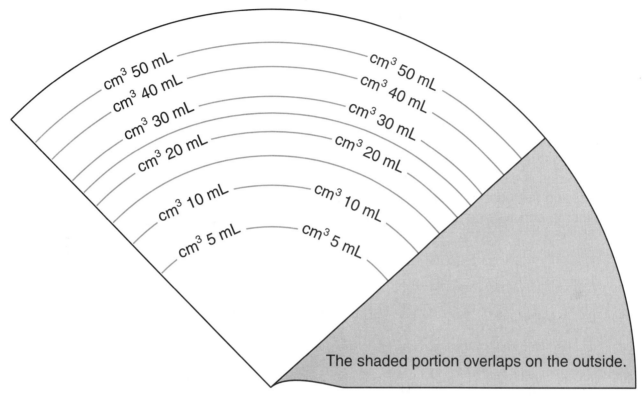

The shaded portion overlaps on the outside.

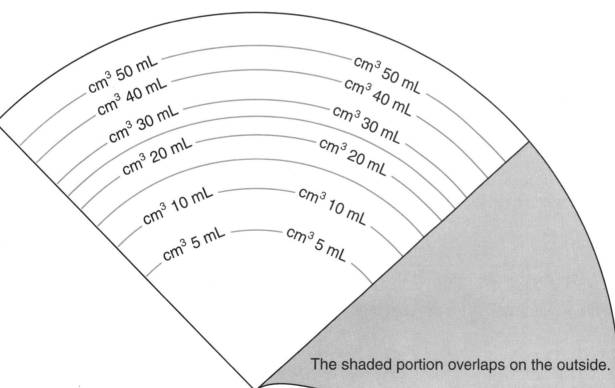

The shaded portion overlaps on the outside.

Cut out one of the cone templates and attach a strip of tape on the back side, as shown.

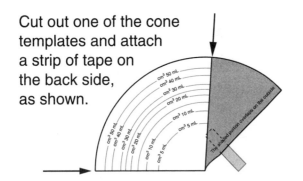

Curl the cone into position, lining up the two heavy black lines and the sets of blue lines.

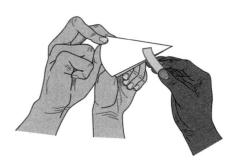

While one partner holds the top edge in position, the other partner pulls the tape to make the lines come together at the apex (tip) of the cone. When all the lines are in the right position, press the tape down, and then use more tape to seal the seams on the inside and outside so that your cone won't leak.

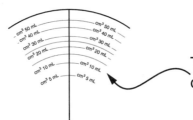

This is how the markings on the inside of your cone should look when it's ready.

just right, black lines and
blue lines matched

Below are examples of some mistakes to avoid.

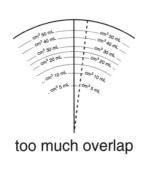

too much overlap

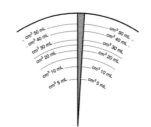

black lines matched at
bottom, but not at top

black lines matched at
top, but not at bottom

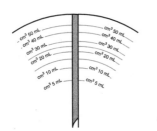

black lines not matched

some blue lines
matched, but not to
the same measures

blue lines
not matched

Rectangular Prism Patterns

Pattern A

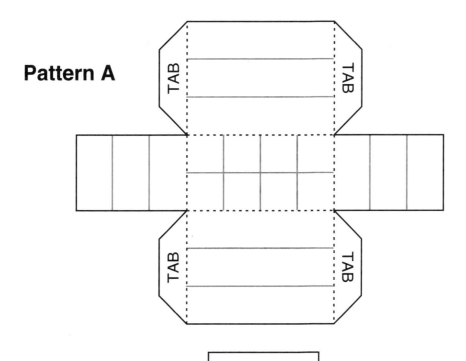

Pattern B

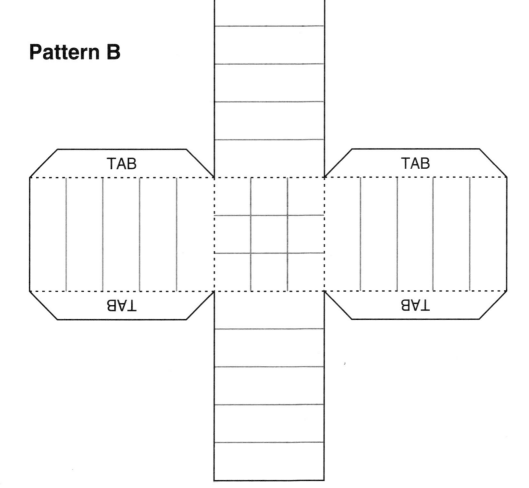

Slide Rule

Assembly Instructions:

1. Cut along the solid lines.

2. Score and fold along the dashed line of the holder so that the number lines are on the outside.

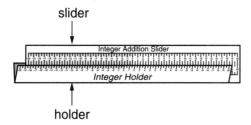

slider

holder

Fraction Subtraction Slider

Fraction Addition Slider

Fraction Holder

Integer Holder

Fraction Addition Slider

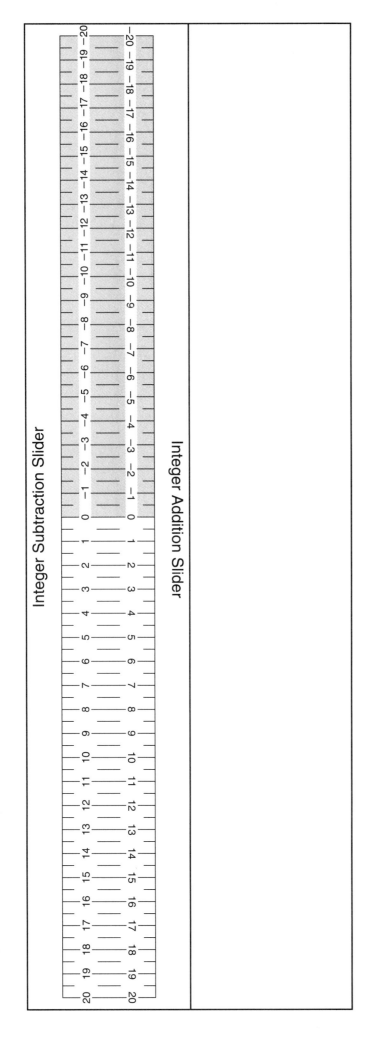

Integer Addition Slider

Integer Subtraction Slider

5-cm Cube Container

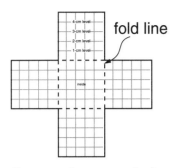

fold line

Cut out the cross below. Using a straightedge and the point of your compass or scissors, score each of the fold lines (the four dashed lines).

Bend up the arms of the cross on the fold lines, so that the grid is on the inside.

Tape the edges together so that they are sealed completely from top to bottom. You will end up with a cube that is open at the top.

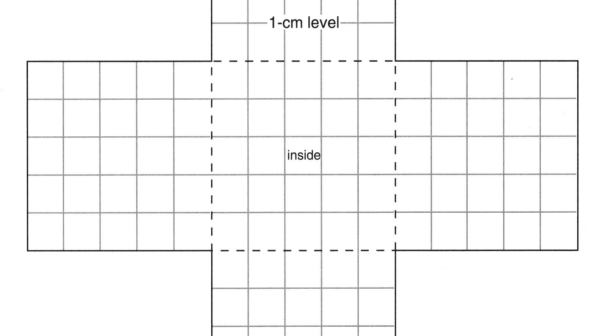

4-cm level

3-cm level

2-cm level

1-cm level

inside

Prism Patterns

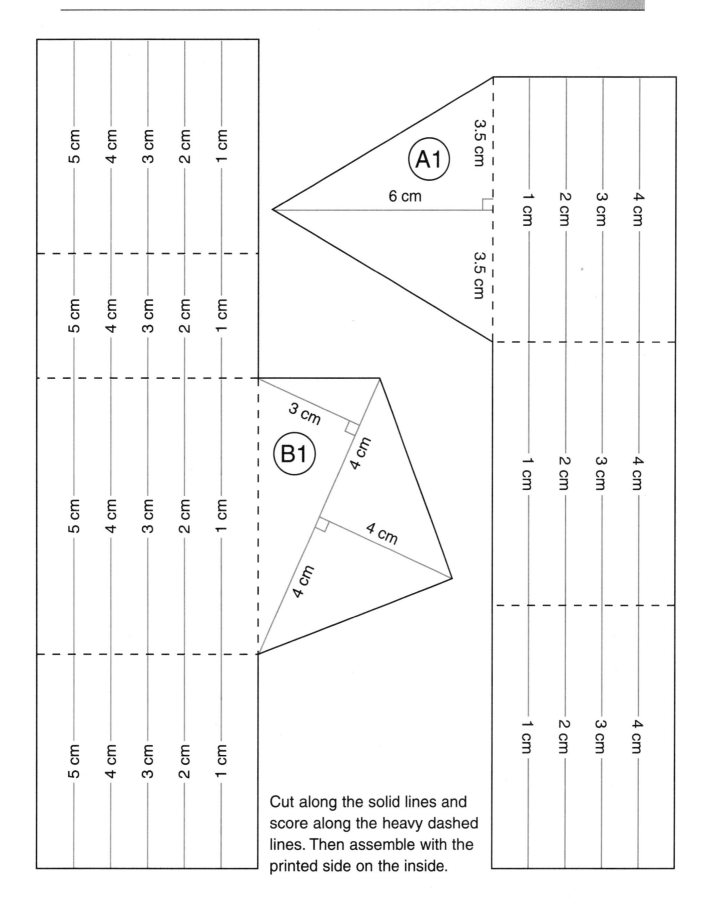

A1

6 cm
3.5 cm
3.5 cm

5 cm 4 cm 3 cm 2 cm 1 cm

5 cm 4 cm 3 cm 2 cm 1 cm

5 cm 4 cm 3 cm 2 cm 1 cm

5 cm 4 cm 3 cm 2 cm 1 cm

1 cm 2 cm 3 cm 4 cm

1 cm 2 cm 3 cm 4 cm

1 cm 2 cm 3 cm 4 cm

B1

3 cm
4 cm
4 cm
4 cm

Cut along the solid lines and
score along the heavy dashed
lines. Then assemble with the
printed side on the inside.

Pyramid Patterns

Cut along the solid lines and score along the heavy dashed lines.

Spoon Scramble Cards

$\frac{1}{4}$ of 24	$\frac{3}{4} * 8$	50% of 12	0.10 $*$ 60
$\frac{1}{3}$ of 21	$3\frac{1}{2} * 2$	25% of 28	0.10 $*$ 70
$\frac{1}{5}$ of 40	$2 * \frac{16}{4}$	1% of 800	0.10 $*$ 80
$\frac{3}{4}$ of 12	$4\frac{1}{2} * 2$	25% of 36	0.10 $*$ 90

Use with Lesson 120 and following.

Reference

Multiplication/Division Facts Table

*,/	1	2	3	4	5	6	7	8	9	10	11	12
1	1	2	3	4	5	6	7	8	9	10	11	12
2	2	4	6	8	10	12	14	16	18	20	22	24
3	3	6	9	12	15	18	21	24	27	30	33	36
4	4	8	12	16	20	24	28	32	36	40	44	48
5	5	10	15	20	25	30	35	40	45	50	55	60
6	6	12	18	24	30	36	42	48	54	60	66	72
7	7	14	21	28	35	42	49	56	63	70	77	84
8	8	16	24	32	40	48	56	64	72	80	88	96
9	9	18	27	36	45	54	63	72	81	90	99	108
10	10	20	30	40	50	60	70	80	90	100	110	120
11	11	22	33	44	55	66	77	88	99	110	121	132
12	12	24	36	48	60	72	84	96	108	120	132	144

"Easy" Fractions	Decimals	Percents
$\frac{1}{2}$	0.50	50%
$\frac{1}{3}$	$0.\overline{3}$	$33\frac{1}{3}\%$
$\frac{2}{3}$	$0.\overline{6}$	$66\frac{2}{3}\%$
$\frac{1}{4}$	0.25	25%
$\frac{3}{4}$	0.75	75%
$\frac{1}{5}$	0.20	20%
$\frac{2}{5}$	0.40	40%
$\frac{3}{5}$	0.60	60%
$\frac{4}{5}$	0.80	80%
$\frac{1}{6}$	$0.1\overline{6}$	$16\frac{2}{3}\%$
$\frac{1}{8}$	0.125	$12\frac{1}{2}\%$
$\frac{3}{8}$	0.375	$37\frac{1}{2}\%$
$\frac{5}{8}$	0.625	$62\frac{1}{2}\%$
$\frac{7}{8}$	0.875	$87\frac{1}{2}\%$
$\frac{1}{10}$	0.10	10%
$\frac{3}{10}$	0.30	30%
$\frac{7}{10}$	0.70	70%
$\frac{9}{10}$	0.90	90%

Prefixes

uni-	one	tera-	trillion (10^{12})
bi-	two	giga-	billion (10^{9})
tri-	three	mega-	million (10^{6})
quad-	four	kilo-	thousand (10^{3})
penta-	five	hecto-	hundred (10^{2})
hexa-	six	deca-	ten (10^{1})
hepta-	seven	uni-	one (10^{0})
octa-	eight	deci-	tenth (10^{-1})
nona-	nine	centi-	hundredth (10^{-2})
deca-	ten	milli-	thousandth (10^{-3})
dodeca-	twelve	micro-	millionth (10^{-6})
icosa-	twenty	nano-	billionth (10^{-9})

Symbols

+	plus or positive	x^{n}	nth power of x	⌐	right angle
−	minus or negative	$\sqrt{x}$	square root of x	⊥	is perpendicular to
*, ×	multiplied by	%	percent	∥	is parallel to
÷, /	divided by	$\frac{a}{b}$, $a{:}b$, a/b	ratio of a to b	$\triangle ABC$	triangle ABC
=	is equal to		or a divided by b	$\angle ABC$	angle ABC
≠	is not equal to		or the fraction $\frac{a}{b}$	$\angle B$	angle B
<	is less than	°	degree		
>	is greater than	(a,b)	ordered pair		
≤	is less than or equal to	$\overleftrightarrow{AS}$	line AS		
≥	is greater than or equal to	$\overline{AS}$	line segment AS		
		$\overrightarrow{AS}$	ray AS		

Metric System

Units of Length

1 kilometer (km)	= 1000 meters (m)
1 meter	= 10 decimeters (dm)
	= 100 centimeters (cm)
	= 1000 millimeters (mm)
1 decimeter	= 10 centimeters
1 centimeter	= 10 millimeters

Units of Area

1 square meter (m^2)	= 100 square decimeters (dm^2)
	= 10,000 square centimeters (cm^2)
1 square decimeter	= 100 square centimeters
1 are (a)	= 100 square meters
1 hectare (ha)	= 100 ares
1 square kilometer (km^2)	= 100 hectares

Units of Volume

1 cubic meter (m^3)	= 1000 cubic decimeters (dm^3)
	= 1,000,000 cubic centimeters (cm^3)
1 cubic decimeter	= 1000 cubic centimeters

Units of Capacity

1 kiloliter (kL)	= 1000 liters (L)
1 liter	= 1000 milliliters (mL)

Units of Mass

1 metric ton (t)	= 1000 kilograms (kg)
1 kilogram	= 1000 grams (g)
1 gram	= 1000 milligrams (mg)

U.S. Customary System

Units of Length

1 mile (mi)	= 1760 yards (yd)
	= 5280 feet (ft)
1 yard	= 3 feet
	= 36 inches (in)
1 foot	= 12 inches

Units of Area

1 square yard (yd^2)	= 9 square feet (ft^2)
	= 1296 square inches (in^2)
1 square foot	= 144 square inches
1 acre	= 43,560 square feet
1 square mile (mi^2)	= 640 acres

Units of Volume

1 cubic yard (yd^3)	= 27 cubic feet (ft^3)
1 cubic foot	= 1728 cubic inches (in^3)

Units of Capacity

1 gallon (gal)	= 4 quarts (qt)
1 quart	= 2 pints (pt)
1 pint	= 2 cups (c)
1 cup	= 8 fluid ounces (fl oz)
1 fluid ounce	= 2 tablespoons (tbs)
1 tablespoon	= 3 teaspoons (tsp)

Units of Weight

1 ton (T)	= 2000 pounds (lb)
1 pound	= 16 ounces (oz)

Units of Time

1 century	= 100 years
1 decade	= 10 years
1 year (yr)	= 12 months
	= 52 weeks (plus one or two days)
	= 365 days (366 days in a leap year)
1 month (mo)	= 28, 29, 30, or 31 days
1 week (wk)	= 7 days
1 day (d)	= 24 hours
1 hour (hr)	= 60 minutes
1 minute (min)	= 60 seconds (sec)

System Equivalents

1 inch is about 2.5 cm (2.54)

1 kilometer is about 0.6 mile (0.621)

1 mile is about 1.6 kilometers (1.609)

1 meter is about 39 inches (39.37)

1 liter is about 1.1 quarts (1.057)

1 ounce is about 28 grams (28.350)

1 kilogram is about 2.2 pounds (2.205)

1 acre is about 2.5 hectares (2.47)

Rules for Order of Operations

1. Do operations within parentheses or other grouping symbols before doing anything else.
2. Calculate all powers.
3. Do multiplications or divisions in order, from left to right.
4. Then do additions or subtractions in order, from left to right.

Place-Value Chart

trillions	100B	10B	billions	100M	10M	millions	hundred-thousands	ten-thousands	thousands	hundreds	tens	ones	.	tenths	hundredths	thousandths
1000 billions			1000 millions			1,000,000s	100,000s	10,000s	1000s	100s	10s	1s	.	0.1s	0.01s	0.001s
10^{12}	10^{11}	10^{10}	10^9	10^8	10^7	10^6	10^5	10^4	10^3	10^2	10^1	10^0	.	10^{-1}	10^{-2}	10^{-3}

Probability Meter

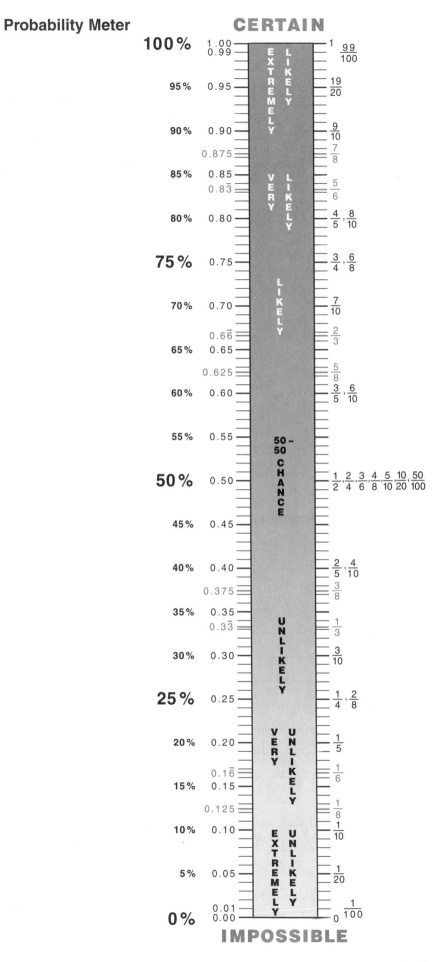

Latitude and Longitude

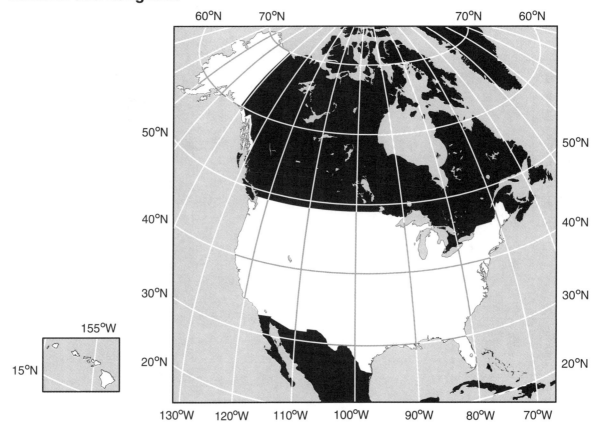

Fraction-Stick and Decimal Number-Line Chart

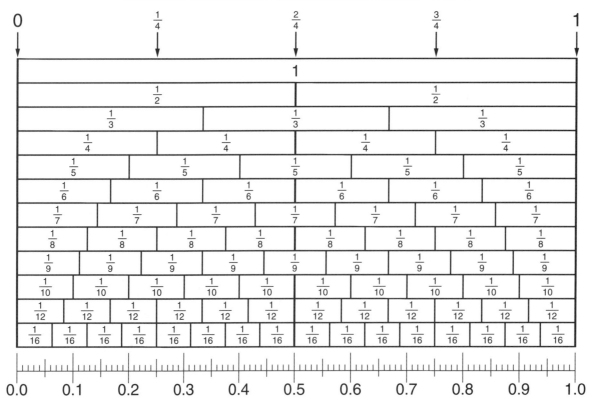

Equivalent Fractions, Decimals, and Percents

															Decimal	Percent
$\frac{1}{2}$	$\frac{2}{4}$	$\frac{3}{6}$	$\frac{4}{8}$	$\frac{5}{10}$	$\frac{6}{12}$	$\frac{7}{14}$	$\frac{8}{16}$	$\frac{9}{18}$	$\frac{10}{20}$	$\frac{11}{22}$	$\frac{12}{24}$	$\frac{13}{26}$	$\frac{14}{28}$	$\frac{15}{30}$	0.5	50%
$\frac{1}{3}$	$\frac{2}{6}$	$\frac{3}{9}$	$\frac{4}{12}$	$\frac{5}{15}$	$\frac{6}{18}$	$\frac{7}{21}$	$\frac{8}{24}$	$\frac{9}{27}$	$\frac{10}{30}$	$\frac{11}{33}$	$\frac{12}{36}$	$\frac{13}{39}$	$\frac{14}{42}$	$\frac{15}{45}$	$0.\overline{3}$	$33\frac{1}{3}$%
$\frac{2}{3}$	$\frac{4}{6}$	$\frac{6}{9}$	$\frac{8}{12}$	$\frac{10}{15}$	$\frac{12}{18}$	$\frac{14}{21}$	$\frac{16}{24}$	$\frac{18}{27}$	$\frac{20}{30}$	$\frac{22}{33}$	$\frac{24}{36}$	$\frac{26}{39}$	$\frac{28}{42}$	$\frac{30}{45}$	$0.\overline{6}$	$66\frac{2}{3}$%
$\frac{1}{4}$	$\frac{2}{8}$	$\frac{3}{12}$	$\frac{4}{16}$	$\frac{5}{20}$	$\frac{6}{24}$	$\frac{7}{28}$	$\frac{8}{32}$	$\frac{9}{36}$	$\frac{10}{40}$	$\frac{11}{44}$	$\frac{12}{48}$	$\frac{13}{52}$	$\frac{14}{56}$	$\frac{15}{60}$	0.25	25%
$\frac{3}{4}$	$\frac{6}{8}$	$\frac{9}{12}$	$\frac{12}{16}$	$\frac{15}{20}$	$\frac{18}{24}$	$\frac{21}{28}$	$\frac{24}{32}$	$\frac{27}{36}$	$\frac{30}{40}$	$\frac{33}{44}$	$\frac{36}{48}$	$\frac{39}{52}$	$\frac{42}{56}$	$\frac{45}{60}$	0.75	75%
$\frac{1}{5}$	$\frac{2}{10}$	$\frac{3}{15}$	$\frac{4}{20}$	$\frac{5}{25}$	$\frac{6}{30}$	$\frac{7}{35}$	$\frac{8}{40}$	$\frac{9}{45}$	$\frac{10}{50}$	$\frac{11}{55}$	$\frac{12}{60}$	$\frac{13}{65}$	$\frac{14}{70}$	$\frac{15}{75}$	0.2	20%
$\frac{2}{5}$	$\frac{4}{10}$	$\frac{6}{15}$	$\frac{8}{20}$	$\frac{10}{25}$	$\frac{12}{30}$	$\frac{14}{35}$	$\frac{16}{40}$	$\frac{18}{45}$	$\frac{20}{50}$	$\frac{22}{55}$	$\frac{24}{60}$	$\frac{26}{65}$	$\frac{28}{70}$	$\frac{30}{75}$	0.4	40%
$\frac{3}{5}$	$\frac{6}{10}$	$\frac{9}{15}$	$\frac{12}{20}$	$\frac{15}{25}$	$\frac{18}{30}$	$\frac{21}{35}$	$\frac{24}{40}$	$\frac{27}{45}$	$\frac{30}{50}$	$\frac{33}{55}$	$\frac{36}{60}$	$\frac{39}{65}$	$\frac{42}{70}$	$\frac{45}{75}$	0.6	60%
$\frac{4}{5}$	$\frac{8}{10}$	$\frac{12}{15}$	$\frac{16}{20}$	$\frac{20}{25}$	$\frac{24}{30}$	$\frac{28}{35}$	$\frac{32}{40}$	$\frac{36}{45}$	$\frac{40}{50}$	$\frac{44}{55}$	$\frac{48}{60}$	$\frac{52}{65}$	$\frac{56}{70}$	$\frac{60}{75}$	0.8	80%
$\frac{1}{6}$	$\frac{2}{12}$	$\frac{3}{18}$	$\frac{4}{24}$	$\frac{5}{30}$	$\frac{6}{36}$	$\frac{7}{42}$	$\frac{8}{48}$	$\frac{9}{54}$	$\frac{10}{60}$	$\frac{11}{66}$	$\frac{12}{72}$	$\frac{13}{78}$	$\frac{14}{84}$	$\frac{15}{90}$	$0.1\overline{6}$	$16\frac{2}{3}$%
$\frac{5}{6}$	$\frac{10}{12}$	$\frac{15}{18}$	$\frac{20}{24}$	$\frac{25}{30}$	$\frac{30}{36}$	$\frac{35}{42}$	$\frac{40}{48}$	$\frac{45}{54}$	$\frac{50}{60}$	$\frac{55}{66}$	$\frac{60}{72}$	$\frac{65}{78}$	$\frac{70}{84}$	$\frac{75}{90}$	$0.8\overline{3}$	$83\frac{1}{3}$%
$\frac{1}{7}$	$\frac{2}{14}$	$\frac{3}{21}$	$\frac{4}{28}$	$\frac{5}{35}$	$\frac{6}{42}$	$\frac{7}{49}$	$\frac{8}{56}$	$\frac{9}{63}$	$\frac{10}{70}$	$\frac{11}{77}$	$\frac{12}{84}$	$\frac{13}{91}$	$\frac{14}{98}$	$\frac{15}{105}$	0.143	14.3%
$\frac{2}{7}$	$\frac{4}{14}$	$\frac{6}{21}$	$\frac{8}{28}$	$\frac{10}{35}$	$\frac{12}{42}$	$\frac{14}{49}$	$\frac{16}{56}$	$\frac{18}{63}$	$\frac{20}{70}$	$\frac{22}{77}$	$\frac{24}{84}$	$\frac{26}{91}$	$\frac{28}{98}$	$\frac{30}{105}$	0.286	28.6%
$\frac{3}{7}$	$\frac{6}{14}$	$\frac{9}{21}$	$\frac{12}{28}$	$\frac{15}{35}$	$\frac{18}{42}$	$\frac{21}{49}$	$\frac{24}{56}$	$\frac{27}{63}$	$\frac{30}{70}$	$\frac{33}{77}$	$\frac{36}{84}$	$\frac{39}{91}$	$\frac{42}{98}$	$\frac{45}{105}$	0.429	42.9%
$\frac{4}{7}$	$\frac{8}{14}$	$\frac{12}{21}$	$\frac{16}{28}$	$\frac{20}{35}$	$\frac{24}{42}$	$\frac{28}{49}$	$\frac{32}{56}$	$\frac{36}{63}$	$\frac{40}{70}$	$\frac{44}{77}$	$\frac{48}{84}$	$\frac{52}{91}$	$\frac{56}{98}$	$\frac{60}{105}$	0.571	57.1%
$\frac{5}{7}$	$\frac{10}{14}$	$\frac{15}{21}$	$\frac{20}{28}$	$\frac{25}{35}$	$\frac{30}{42}$	$\frac{35}{49}$	$\frac{40}{56}$	$\frac{45}{63}$	$\frac{50}{70}$	$\frac{55}{77}$	$\frac{60}{84}$	$\frac{65}{91}$	$\frac{70}{98}$	$\frac{75}{105}$	0.714	71.4%
$\frac{6}{7}$	$\frac{12}{14}$	$\frac{18}{21}$	$\frac{24}{28}$	$\frac{30}{35}$	$\frac{36}{42}$	$\frac{42}{49}$	$\frac{48}{56}$	$\frac{54}{63}$	$\frac{60}{70}$	$\frac{66}{77}$	$\frac{72}{84}$	$\frac{78}{91}$	$\frac{84}{98}$	$\frac{90}{105}$	0.857	85.7%
$\frac{1}{8}$	$\frac{2}{16}$	$\frac{3}{24}$	$\frac{4}{32}$	$\frac{5}{40}$	$\frac{6}{48}$	$\frac{7}{56}$	$\frac{8}{64}$	$\frac{9}{72}$	$\frac{10}{80}$	$\frac{11}{88}$	$\frac{12}{96}$	$\frac{13}{104}$	$\frac{14}{112}$	$\frac{15}{120}$	0.125	$12\frac{1}{2}$%
$\frac{3}{8}$	$\frac{6}{16}$	$\frac{9}{24}$	$\frac{12}{32}$	$\frac{15}{40}$	$\frac{18}{48}$	$\frac{21}{56}$	$\frac{24}{64}$	$\frac{27}{72}$	$\frac{30}{80}$	$\frac{33}{88}$	$\frac{36}{96}$	$\frac{39}{104}$	$\frac{42}{112}$	$\frac{45}{120}$	0.375	$37\frac{1}{2}$%
$\frac{5}{8}$	$\frac{10}{16}$	$\frac{15}{24}$	$\frac{20}{32}$	$\frac{25}{40}$	$\frac{30}{48}$	$\frac{35}{56}$	$\frac{40}{64}$	$\frac{45}{72}$	$\frac{50}{80}$	$\frac{55}{88}$	$\frac{60}{96}$	$\frac{65}{104}$	$\frac{70}{112}$	$\frac{75}{120}$	0.625	$62\frac{1}{2}$%
$\frac{7}{8}$	$\frac{14}{16}$	$\frac{21}{24}$	$\frac{28}{32}$	$\frac{35}{40}$	$\frac{42}{48}$	$\frac{49}{56}$	$\frac{56}{64}$	$\frac{63}{72}$	$\frac{70}{80}$	$\frac{77}{88}$	$\frac{84}{96}$	$\frac{91}{104}$	$\frac{98}{112}$	$\frac{105}{120}$	0.875	$87\frac{1}{2}$%
$\frac{1}{9}$	$\frac{2}{18}$	$\frac{3}{27}$	$\frac{4}{36}$	$\frac{5}{45}$	$\frac{6}{54}$	$\frac{7}{63}$	$\frac{8}{72}$	$\frac{9}{81}$	$\frac{10}{90}$	$\frac{11}{99}$	$\frac{12}{108}$	$\frac{13}{117}$	$\frac{14}{126}$	$\frac{15}{135}$	$0.\overline{1}$	$11\frac{1}{9}$%
$\frac{2}{9}$	$\frac{4}{18}$	$\frac{6}{27}$	$\frac{8}{36}$	$\frac{10}{45}$	$\frac{12}{54}$	$\frac{14}{63}$	$\frac{16}{72}$	$\frac{18}{81}$	$\frac{20}{90}$	$\frac{22}{99}$	$\frac{24}{108}$	$\frac{26}{117}$	$\frac{28}{126}$	$\frac{30}{135}$	$0.\overline{2}$	$22\frac{2}{9}$%
$\frac{4}{9}$	$\frac{8}{18}$	$\frac{12}{27}$	$\frac{16}{36}$	$\frac{20}{45}$	$\frac{24}{54}$	$\frac{28}{63}$	$\frac{32}{72}$	$\frac{36}{81}$	$\frac{40}{90}$	$\frac{44}{99}$	$\frac{48}{108}$	$\frac{52}{117}$	$\frac{56}{126}$	$\frac{60}{135}$	$0.\overline{4}$	$44\frac{4}{9}$%
$\frac{5}{9}$	$\frac{10}{18}$	$\frac{15}{27}$	$\frac{20}{36}$	$\frac{25}{45}$	$\frac{30}{54}$	$\frac{35}{63}$	$\frac{40}{72}$	$\frac{45}{81}$	$\frac{50}{90}$	$\frac{55}{99}$	$\frac{60}{108}$	$\frac{65}{117}$	$\frac{70}{126}$	$\frac{75}{135}$	$0.\overline{5}$	$55\frac{5}{9}$%
$\frac{7}{9}$	$\frac{14}{18}$	$\frac{21}{27}$	$\frac{28}{36}$	$\frac{35}{45}$	$\frac{42}{54}$	$\frac{49}{63}$	$\frac{56}{72}$	$\frac{63}{81}$	$\frac{70}{90}$	$\frac{77}{99}$	$\frac{84}{108}$	$\frac{91}{117}$	$\frac{98}{126}$	$\frac{105}{135}$	$0.\overline{7}$	$77\frac{7}{9}$%
$\frac{8}{9}$	$\frac{16}{18}$	$\frac{24}{27}$	$\frac{32}{36}$	$\frac{40}{45}$	$\frac{48}{54}$	$\frac{56}{63}$	$\frac{64}{72}$	$\frac{72}{81}$	$\frac{80}{90}$	$\frac{88}{99}$	$\frac{96}{108}$	$\frac{104}{117}$	$\frac{112}{126}$	$\frac{120}{135}$	$0.\overline{8}$	$88\frac{8}{9}$%

Note: The decimals for sevenths have been rounded to the nearest thousandth.

Prism Patterns (continued)

Cut along the solid lines and score along the heavy dashed lines.
Then assemble with the printed side on the inside.

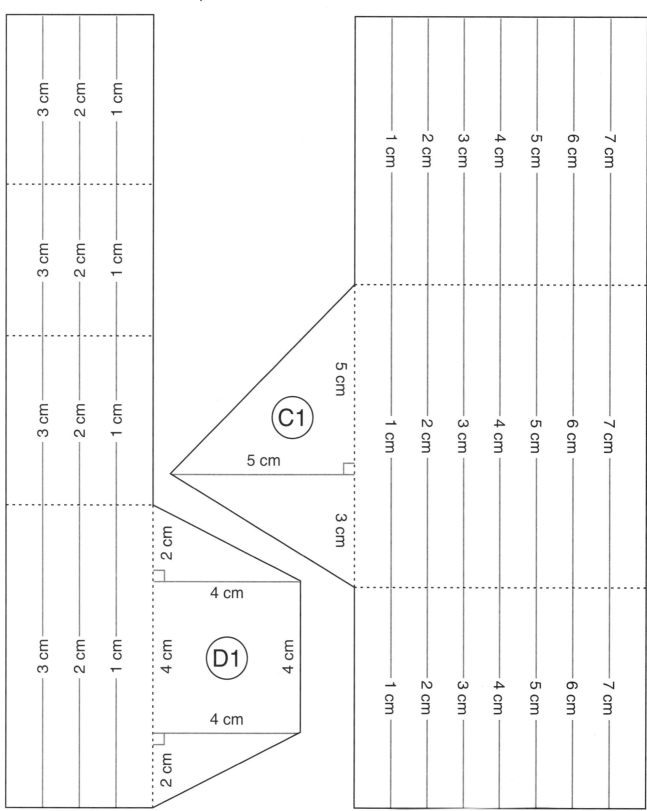